Practice
FCC-Type Exams
for
Radiotelephone Operator's
License
Second Class

Practice
FCC-Type Exams
for
Radiotelephone Operator's
License
Second Class

RICHARD J. SMITH
Applications Engineering Manager

VICTOR F. C. VELEY
Dean of Communications Science
Grantham School of Engineering

Radio Communications and Electronics Instructor
Mount San Antonio College

Consulting Editor
Milton Kaufman
author of
Radio Operator's License Q & A Manual

HAYDEN BOOK COMPANY, INC.
Rochelle Park, New Jersey

Library of Congress Cataloging in Publication Data

Smith, Richard J
    Practice FCC-type exams for radiotelephone operator's
license, second class.

    1. Radiotelephone--Examinations, questions, etc.
2. Radio operators--United States. I. Veley, Victor F. C.,
joint author. II. Kaufman, Milton. Radio operator's license
Q and A manual. III. Title.
TK6554.5.S53   621.3845'076   75-31537
ISBN 0-8104-5965-5

        4   5   6   7   8   9   PRINTING

        78 79 80 81 82 83   YEAR

Preface

Instructors in the communications field have long been aware that practice workbooks, as well as good texts, are necessary if students are going to learn the required subjects successfully enough to pass the FCC examinations. This workbook has been prepared as a learning tool that will serve as a means of self-evaluation for communications technicians preparing for the Second Class Radiotelephone Operator's License. It can be used for self-study or for classroom study. It is not intended to replace present text books, but rather to reinforce what has been studied in the text and to prepare the student for his FCC examination.

This workbook has been prepared on the assumption that the student has obtained his Third Class Operator's License, which requires passing Elements 1 and 2. The workbook contains nine practice tests of 100 questions each for Element 3 (Basic Radiotelephone) and two tests of 50 questions each for Element 8 (Ship Radar Techniques), for students desiring a radar endorsement.

Answers with study references and discussions of difficult points are found in the back of the book, in addition to an answer sheet merely listing the correct choices for the questions. Most of the mathematical problems are individually solved. This workbook was specifically written as a companion to Milton Kaufman's Radio Operator's License Q & A Manual, * but may also be used with any text that follows the FCC Study Guide numbers, or any text whose numbering scheme differs from the FCC Study Guide, although in this case the reference numbers would not be valid. For the convenience of the student, a glossary is provided at the end of the book.

The student should first study the material for Element 3 from his text. He should then read the introductory material of this workbook before taking Test 1. Convenient spaces are provided for the answers. The student should then use the answer sheet located at the back of the book to correct his test. Any questions missed should be reviewed, using the text and referenced answers. This same procedure is to be followed for Tests 2 through 9 for Element 3. Should the student desire to prepare himself to take the Ship Radar Techniques test to obtain the radar endorsement, then he should follow the same procedures as above for Element 8, Tests 1 and 2.

The FCC passing grade is 75%. The student should average 85% or better in this workbook to achieve the level of confidence needed to take the FCC test. It is suggested that if his average score for Tests 1 through 9 is below 85%, he should repeat his study of his text and try again. The same approach applies to the Ship Radar Techniques Tests 1 and 2.

The authors wish to thank Milton Kaufman, their consulting editor, for his review of this book, which greatly contributed to the accuracy of its contents.

Richard J. Smith

Victor F. C. Veley

* Hayden Book Company, Inc., Rochelle Park, N.J.

Taking the FCC Examination

1. Get a full night's sleep. The benefits to be gained by a few extra hours of study are often more than offset by the detrimental effects of fatigue.

2. Don't review or study on the morning of the test. You may lose confidence in your ability and not do so well on the test. Make sure that you leave yourself adequate time to reach the testing center before the doors open.

3. Prepare yourself mentally. Remember that for the Element 3 examination you may miss 25 questions and still pass; you may miss 12 questions for the Element 8 examination and still pass.

4. Take along only the following items when you go into the FCC examination room (no other items are permitted in the room while an exam is in progress):
   a. Two sharp pencils and one ball-point pen.
   b. Chewing gum or life-savers to subdue tension (no smoking is allowed).
   c. The exact cash amount of $4.00 for the Second Class License testing fee. If a radar endorsement is desired, there is an additional fee of $2.00.
   d. Your valid Third Class License.
   e. A slide rule or pocket calculator may be used provided they do not have mathematical formulas printed on them.

5. Wear comfortable clothes since you will be sitting for a considerable length of time. (Note that the FCC examiner will not allow you to leave the testing room to go to the restroom.)

6. You will have ample time to take the examination (all day if you wish). No points are given for being the first to complete the examination. Take your time and strive for accuracy.

7. It is suggested that the questions should be answered in the following order:
   a. Rules and Regulations and definitions of terms.
   b. Theory questions.
   c. Problems involving mathematics. If you attempt these first, you may become fatigued and then you may answer some of the easier questions incorrectly.
   d. The first time around, skip all questions that seem difficult, and answer these last. However, make certain that every question has been answered even if you have to guess.
   e. Take time to recheck and make sure that all your answers have been placed in the correct letter space of your choice.

8. Put your thoughts down on the scratch paper provided, and do not attempt to work any mathematical problems in your head. Working these problems out on paper is slower but far more accurate.

9. Some of the questions will be similar to those you have taken in the practice tests. However, there may be subtle differences, so do not attempt to recall the answers given in the practice tests but concentrate on the actual FCC question.

Taking a Multiple Choice Test

1. Directions on the FCC answer sheets will indicate the method of marking your selected answer. As an example, if your selection is "B" make a mark in the space provided as shown:

   (a) | | (b) ■   (c) | | (d) | | (e) | |

   Be sure to follow these directions when taking your FCC examinations. They may use a correction machine to correct your test, and without the proper marking, it may not give you credit for a proper answer.

2. First read the question while covering up the five multiple choice answers, and attempt to find the correct solution. Then read the question again, very carefully, in conjunction with each of the five possible answers. In particular, watch out for expressions such as "not true," "not false," "incorrect," etc.

3. Remember that more than one of the answers may be correct, and that this situation will be covered by still another one of the possible answers, such as "Both (a) and (b) are true" or "All of the above are true." In addition, the first four answers may be false, and the fifth answer stating that "None of the above are true" would therefore be correct.

4. Check every answer carefully to make certain that you have correctly indicated your choice. In other words, if your choice is in fact "b", make sure you have not marked "d". This is a very common type of error with questions that are inaccurately answered in the actual FCC examination.

5. If you answer a question incorrectly in this workbook, use the references to find why the answer as given is correct and why your answer was wrong.

Study Tips

1. Develop good study habits. Provide yourself with a quiet place and plan to study one hour or more every day. Have ready all materials necessary. Use an electronics dictionary or a glossary to look up unfamiliar terms and phrases. You must know the proper definition of words and terms to know what is being asked in a question and to select the proper answer.
2. Develop accuracy in placing your answer on the answer sheet. You would be surprised at the number of students who know the proper answer but place it in the wrong space.
3. Do not try to memorize answers (except possibly for the "Rules and Regulations") but try to understand the background of each question.
4. Use a pencil rather than a pen to solve problems. Keep your mathematical work in a neat order. If you solve a mathematical problem incorrectly, you will then be able to find your errors more easily.
5. Make a thorough review after each test of the questions you have missed, using the text and answer sheets as reference material.

Contents

Element 3, Test 1

1. The circuit shown in Fig. 1 is a transistorized:
(a) Clapp oscillator.
(b) Colpitts oscillator.
(c) Pierce oscillator.
(d) Hartley oscillator.
(e) electron-coupled oscillator.

(a) I I (b) I I (c) I I (d) I I (e) I I

2. In Fig. 1 of Question 1, what is the purpose of the capacitor across the base resistor?
(a) To determine the operating frequency of the circuit.
(b) To provide a low-impedance path so the base is effectively at ground potential at the radio frequency of operation.
(c) To increase the stability of the dc base bias voltage.
(d) To stabilize the collector voltage.
(e) The capacitor is not required and should be removed.

(a) I I (b) I I (c) I I (d) I I (e) I I

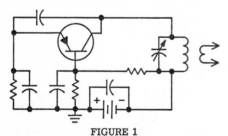

FIGURE 1

3. What is the best type of instrument for measuring RF currents?
(a) A VTVM.
(b) A VOM.
(c) A galvanometer.
(d) A moving vane meter.
(e) A thermocouple meter.

(a) I I (b) I I (c) I I (d) I I (e) I I

4. Which statement is the most correct about the circuit shown in Fig. 2?

(a) The input and output signals will be 180° out of phase.
(b) E1 should be reversed.
(c) There is no phase shift in this circuit.
(d) The circuit shown is in the common emitter configuration.
(e) This circuit is not useful since there is no voltage gain.

(a) I I (b) I I (c) I I (d) I I (e) I I

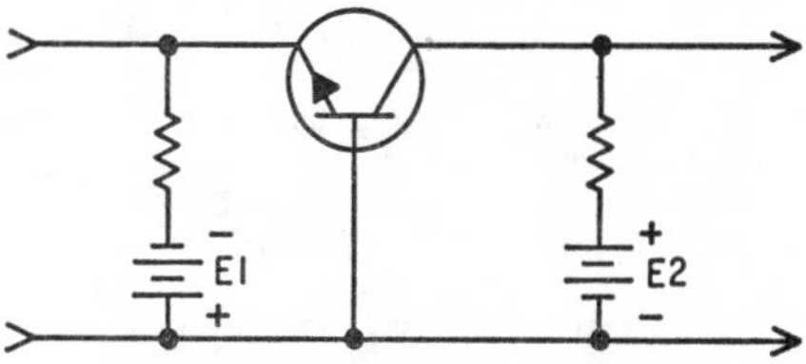

FIGURE 2

5. If an RF inductor is added in series with a whip antenna:
(a) the resonant frequency of the antenna proper is increased.
(b) the operating (resonant) frequency of the antenna is lowered.
(c) the antenna cannot be operated at any frequency.
(d) the transmitter is protected against lightning discharge.
(e) the harmonic radiation from the antenna is reduced.

(a) I I (b) I I (c) I I (d) I I (e) I I

6. Grid bias on the control grid of a class "A" audio amplifier is used to:
(a) control the plate voltage.
(b) control the amplifier gain.
(c) fix the operating point at the center of the transfer characteristic curve.
(d) increase grid current flow.
(e) None of the above.

(a) I I (b) I I (c) I I (d) I I (e) I I

7. Stub-tuning cannot be used:
(a) to reduce radiation loss on a transmission line.

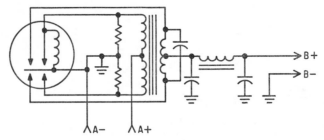

FIGURE 3

(b) to reduce standing waves.
(c) to tune out the reactive component of the antenna load.
(d) as a high-pass filter to reduce unwanted harmonics.
(e) to match the antenna to the surge impedance of the line.

(a) I I   (b) I I   (c) I I   (d) I I   (e) I I

8. A common emitter class "A" amplifier utilizes emitter bias with a PNP transistor. Which statement is not true?
(a) The base must be negative with respect to the emitter.
(b) The emitter is negative with respect to the positive terminal of the battery.
(c) The base will be more positive than the collector.
(d) The collector is negative with respect to the emitter.
(e) The emitter is positive with respect to the positive terminal of the battery.

(a) I I   (b) I I   (c) I I   (d) I I   (e) I I

9. The primary item that affects the alpha-cutoff frequency of a transistor is the:
(a) base thickness.
(b) size of the collector.
(c) size of the emitter.
(d) amount of current due to collector bias.
(e) None of the above are true.

(a) I I   (b) I I   (c) I I   (d) I I   (e) I I

10. A triode amplifier has the following operating conditions: filament voltage, 6.3 V; filament current, 0.3 A; B+, 250 V; i_b; 30 mA; e_c, -5 V. When the plate dissipation is 6 watts, the plate efficiency will be:
(a) 10%   (b) 20%   (c) 30%   (d) 40%
(e) 80%

(a) I I   (b) I I   (c) I I   (d) I I   (e) I I

11. For Land Transportation Service Stations, the transmitter must be checked by a first-class or second-class license holder after:
(a) one week of operation.
(b) a control circuit has been changed.

(c) a new antenna has been installed.
(d) an audio tube has been replaced (AM transmitter).
(e) a new microphone cord has been installed.

(a) I I   (b) I I   (c) I I   (d) I I   (e) I I

12. The soft iron core in a power transformer is laminated to:
(a) reduce iron losses.
(b) reduce dielectric loss.
(c) reduce hysteresis loss.
(d) reduce copper losses.
(e) improve the step-up ratio.

(a) I I   (b) I I   (c) I I   (d) I I   (e) I I

13. Power amplifiers use lower μ triodes than voltage amplifiers because:
(a) a lower μ is associated with a lower r_p which means that a greater power output is possible.
(b) lower μ triodes have a greater input signal-amplitude handling capacity.
(c) less grid bias is necessary.
(d) lower μ triodes have a higher input impedance.
(e) Both (a) and (b) are true.

(a) I I   (b) I I   (c) I I   (d) I I   (e) I I

14. The schematic shown in Fig. 3 is a:
(a) synchronous vibrator power supply.
(b) bridge rectifier.
(c) dc to dc converter.
(d) nonsynchronous vibrator.
(e) Both (a) and (c) are correct.

(a) I I   (b) I I   (c) I I   (d) I I   (e) I I

15. The circuit shown in Fig. 4 represents.
(a) capacitive coupling.
(b) impedance coupling.
(c) L-C coupling.

FIGURE 4

(d) an RF transformer with tuned primary-secondary.

(e) AF transformer coupling.

(a) | | (b) | | (c) | | (d) | | (e) | |

16. The total capacitance between the control grid of an amplifier and ground is called the:

(a) input capacitance.

(b) grid capacitance.

(c) output capacitance.

(d) tube capacitance.

(e) interelectrode capacitance.

(a) | | (b) | | (c) | | (d) | | (e) | |

17. The schematic shown in Fig. 5 represents a frequency multiplier followed by the output stage of a short wave communications transmitter. Both stages have been tuned and are operating correctly. M1, M2, M3 and M4 are dc current meters. The reading of M2 suddenly increases. Which of the following is a possible cause?

(a) The filament of V1 is open.

(b) C4 is an open circuit.

(c) R6 is an open circuit.

(d) L2 is an open circuit.

(e) C3 is an open circuit.

(a) | | (b) | | (c) | | (d) | | (e) | |

18. In Fig. 5 of Question 17, the drive or excitation from the previous stage falls to zero. Which of the following would occur?

(a) M1 would read zero.

(b) M1 would fall to a lower value.

(c) M2 would remain the same.

(d) M4 would decrease sharply.

(e) M2 would decrease sharply.

(a) | | (b) | | (c) | | (d) | | (e) | |

19. In Fig. 5 of Question 17, if a short appears across the secondary of T1, which of the following would occur?

(a) M4 would "dip" sharply.

(b) M4 would fall to zero.

(c) The sideband power would vanish.

(d) The harmonic output would increase.

(e) The average carrier power output would be decreased.

(a) | | (b) | | (c) | | (d) | | (e) | |

20. In Fig. 5 of Question 17, the RF output falls to zero. Which of the following is a possible cause?

(a) The filament of V2 is an open circuit.

(b) R11 is an open circuit.

(c) R13 is an open circuit.

(d) C12 is a short circuit.

(e) A short circuit is across the secondary of T1.

(a) | | (b) | | (c) | | (d) | | (e) | |

21. In Fig. 5 of Question 17, if C2 is shorted, which of the following would occur?

(a) M2 would decrease sharply.

(b) M3 would be zero.

(c) M4 would increase sharply.

(d) V1 would never conduct.

(e) Both (b) and (c) are correct.

(a) | | (b) | | (c) | | (d) | | (e) | |

22. In Fig. 5 of Question 17, if resistor R4 is open, which of the following would occur?

(a) M2 would decrease.

(b) M2 would increase.

(c) M3 would increase.

(d) M3 would decrease.

(e) An increased possibility of parasitic oscillations would exist.

(a) | | (b) | | (c) | | (d) | | (e) | |

23. In Fig. 5 of Question 17, the reading of M2 rises sharply. Which of the following is a possible cause?

(a) A short circuit is across C3.

(b) A short circuit is across L3.

(c) A short circuit is across C4.

(d) C4 is an open circuit.

(e) A short circuit is across R3.

(a) | | (b) | | (c) | | (d) | | (e) | |

24. In Fig. 5 of Question 17, the reading of M4 rises sharply. Which of the following is a possible cause?

(a) The heater filament of V1 is open.

(b) C5 is short circuited.

(c) C9 is an open circuit.

(d) R8 is an open circuit.

(e) All the above are possible causes.

(a) | | (b) | | (c) | | (d) | | (e) | |

25. In Fig. 5 of Question 17, the meter reading of M3 falls to a low value. Which of the following is a possible cause?

(a) There is a short across resistor R8.

(b) There is a short across resistor R1.

(c) C3 is a short circuit.

(d) L2 is an open circuit.

(e) R3 is an open circuit.

(a) | | (b) | | (c) | | (d) | | (e) | |

26. In Fig. 5 of Question 17, if a short circuit develops across C14, which of the following would occur?

(a) The harmonic content in the RF power output would increase.

(b) The RF power output would increase.

(c) M4 would fall sharply.

(d) The RF power output would fall to zero.

(e) A change in the surge impedance of the transmission line would occur.

(a) | | (b) | | (c) | | (d) | | (e) | |

27. In Fig. 5 of Question 17, R3 becomes an open circuit. Which of the following would occur?

(a) M4 would fall sharply.

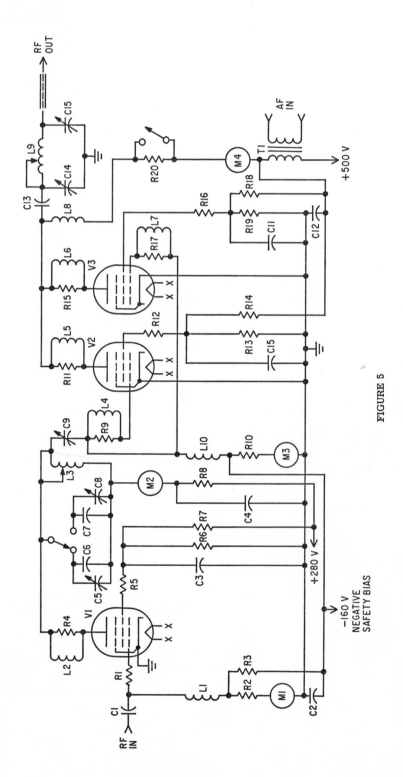

FIGURE 5

(b) M4 would rise sharply.
(c) The RF power output would decrease considerably.
(d) No appreciable change in the RF power output would occur.
(e) The RF output power would increase appreciably.

(a) I I   (b) I I   (c) I I   (d) I I   (e) I I

28. In Fig. 5 of Question 17, the reading of M2 falls to zero. Which of the following is a possible cause?
(a) C3 is a short circuit.
(b) There is a short across R8.
(c) R4 is an open circuit.
(d) R3 is an open circuit.
(e) There is a short across L3.

(a) I I   (b) I I   (c) I I   (d) I I   (e) I I

29. Waveguide sections that are long and horizontal should be:
(a) mounted as level as possible to reduce reflection effects.
(b) circular in order to maintain the direction of polarization.
(c) mounted with a slight incline to prevent moisture from collecting in them.
(d) flexible.
(e) None of the above are true.

(a) I I   (b) I I   (c) I I   (d) I I   (e) I I

30. Type A3 emission is designated as:
(a) television picture transmission.
(b) telegraphic transmission.
(c) telephony, double sideband.
(d) facsimile transmission.
(e) continuous wave (CW).

(a) I I   (b) I I   (c) I I   (d) I I   (e) I I

31. Parasitic oscillations may be eliminated by:
(a) connecting a low value resistor in series with the plate.
(b) connecting a low value resistor in series with the control grid and screen grid, if present.
(c) connecting a small inductor in series with the plate.
(d) connecting a small inductor in series with the control grid.
(e) All of the above are true.

(a) I I   (b) I I   (c) I I   (d) I I   (e) I I

32. What circuit could be used to obtain 100V dc from a 500 V dc supply?
(a) A synchronous vibrator.
(b) A bridge rectifier.
(c) A mechanical inverter.
(d) A step-down transformer.
(e) A bleeder voltage divider.

(a) I I   (b) I I   (c) I I   (d) I I   (e) I I

33. A synchronous vibrator supply has two sets of contacts. The purpose of the second set is to:

(a) act as a mechanical rectifier.
(b) change dc to ac.
(c) reduce the arc at the vibrator terminals.
(d) reduce the RF interference.
(e) Both (c) and (d) are correct.

(a) I I   (b) I I   (c) I I   (d) I I   (e) I I

34. The wavelength of a 40 MHz RF carrier wave in free space is:
(a) 7.5 m   (b) 40 m   (c) 12 m
(d) 13.3 m   (e) 4 m

(a) I I   (b) I I   (c) I I   (d) I I   (e) I I

35. A sky wave frequency of 20 MHz enters the ionosphere. Which layer refracts the wave back to earth?
(a) The D layer.
(b) The E layer.
(c) The Heaviside layer.
(d) The F layer.
(e) None of the above are true.

(a) I I   (b) I I   (c) I I   (d) I I   (e) I I

36. When measuring the dc collector to ground voltage in the circuit shown in Fig. 6, the base is accidentally shorted to ground. Which of the following will occur?
(a) The transistor will be severely damaged.
(b) The collector voltage will not change.
(c) The collector voltage will be more positive.
(d) The collector voltage will be less positive.
(e) The collector voltage will be negative.

(a) I I   (b) I I   (c) I I   (d) I I   (e) I I

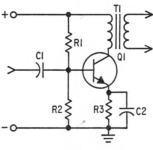

FIGURE 6

37. In Fig. 6 of Question 36, if the forward bias on Q1 is found to be low but the collector current reads high, which of the following is a possible cause?
(a) The transistor has an emitter-to-collector short.
(b) R1 is an open circuit.
(c) R3 is an open circuit.
(d) C1 is an open circuit.
(e) Transformer T1 has a short circuit across the primary.

(a) I I   (b) I I   (c) I I   (d) I I   (e) I I

38. Temperature stabilization is desirable in a transistorized circuit to:
(a) eliminate negative current feedback in the circuit.
(b) stabilize the power supply demands with changes in load current.
(c) stabilize the collector current with changes in temperature.
(d) prevent parasitic oscillations within the circuit.
(e) broaden the frequency response of the circuit.

(a) I I   (b) I I   (c) I I   (d) I I   (e) I I

39. A coil of 5 ohms resistance carries a current of 0.1 A when connected across a 110 V, 60 Hz supply. What is the impedance of the coil?
(a) 5 ohms   (b) 1100 ohms
(c) 550 ohms   (d) 1105 ohms
(e) 1095 ohms

(a) I I   (b) I I   (c) I I   (d) I I   (e) I I

40. When using a grid-dip meter to adjust a resonant circuit to resonance, resonance is indicated when the grid-dip meter's:
(a) grid current is decreased.
(b) resonance indicator light is turned on.
(c) grid current is increased.
(d) cathode current is reduced to zero.
(e) None of the above are true.

(a) I I   (b) I I   (c) I I   (d) I I   (e) I I

41. The field of a shunt wound dc motor becomes open while running under no load. What would be the result?
(a) The motor would continue to run properly.
(b) The motor would stop running.
(c) The motor would race at an ever-increasing speed.
(d) The amount of torque would decrease, and the amount of current flow would decrease.
(e) The motor rpm would decrease, and then the motor would stop running.

(a) I I   (b) I I   (c) I I   (d) I I   (e) I I

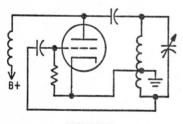

FIGURE 7

42. The circuit shown in Fig. 7 is a:
(a) series-fed Colpitts oscillator.
(b) shunt-fed Colpitts oscillator.

(c) series-fed Hartley oscillator.
(d) shunt-fed Hartley oscillator.
(e) series-fed Armstrong oscillator.

(a) I I   (b) I I   (c) I I   (d) I I   (e) I I

43. A class C amplifier:
(a) does not distort the input signal if the plate load is a resistor.
(b) has a lower input signal amplitude handling capacity than a class B amplifier.
(c) always uses cathode bias.
(d) has a low plate efficiency.
(e) may be operated with signal bias.

(a) I I   (b) I I   (c) I I   (d) I I   (e) I I

44. A low pass filter can:
(a) attenuate harmonics.
(b) attenuate low frequencies.
(c) increase the gain at high frequencies.
(d) eliminate dc from the output.
(e) never be used in receiver circuits.

(a) I I   (b) I I   (c) I I   (d) I I   (e) I I

45. In the Q meter, an RF VTVM is connected across a capacitor which is part of a series LC circuit. The input RF voltage is held constant as the series capacitor is varied. Resonance of the coil under test will be indicated on the VTVM by a:
(a) zero reading.
(b) minimum reading.
(c) sudden dip.
(d) sharp rise to a value which is Q times the input voltage.
(e) None of the above.

(a) I I   (b) I I   (c) I I   (d) I I   (e) I I

46. A superregenerative receiver:
(a) has high sensitivity.
(b) low gain, when compared with a superheterodyne receiver.
(c) may radiate interference signals.
(d) is rarely used in modern communications.
(e) All the above are true.

(a) I I   (b) I I   (c) I I   (d) I I   (e) I I

47. The temperature coefficient of a crystal is +15 Hz per MHz per ^oC. The crystal frequency is 3 MHz at 25^oC and the oscillator is followed by three doubler stages. If the temperature should rise to 40^oC, the transmitter's output frequency would be:
(a) 24,000,000 Hz
(b) 24,005,400 Hz
(c) 24,000,675 Hz
(d) 23,994,600 Hz
(e) 23,999,325 Hz

(a) I I   (b) I I   (c) I I   (d) I I   (e) I I

48. If an FM transmitter is indirectly phase modulated, what circuit is required to

correct the phase modulation to true frequency modulation?
(a) An audio correction network.
(b) A phasitron tube.
(c) The pre-emphasis network.
(d) A limiter stage.
(e) An AFC circuit.

(a) | | (b) | | (c) | | (d) | | (e) | |

49. One characteristic of a shunt-wound dc motor is:
(a) the low efficiency.
(b) the high current drawn from the supply.
(c) the constant speed with changes of load.
(d) that the speed may be controlled by a rheostat in series with the armature.
(e) that no starting box is necessary.

(a) | | (b) | | (c) | | (d) | | (e) | |

50. Which of the following audio amplifiers provides the highest power output with acceptable distortion?
(a) A class A push-pull amplifier using cathode bias.
(b) A class B push-pull amplifier with fixed bias.
(c) A class A amplifier using two tubes in parallel.
(d) A class A amplifier using a beam power tube.
(e) A class A cathode follower.

(a) | | (b) | | (c) | | (d) | | (e) | |

51. A relay:
(a) is a type of wirewound resistor.
(b) has zero inductance.
(c) can be used as a form of switch.
(d) uses a copper armature.
(e) is a type of time-delay resistor.

(a) | | (b) | | (c) | | (d) | | (e) | |

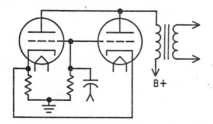

FIGURE 8

52. The circuit shown in Fig. 8 represents:
(a) tubes in push-pull.
(b) tubes in push-push.
(c) tubes in parallel.
(d) a class C power output stage.
(e) tubes in pull-pull.

(a) | | (b) | | (c) | | (d) | | (e) | |

53. The length of the skip distance is dependent on:

(a) the transmitter's frequency.
(b) the density of the ionosphere.
(c) the type of ground over which the wave is passing.
(d) the radio wave's plane of polarization.
(e) Both (a) and (b) are true.

(a) | | (b) | | (c) | | (d) | | (e) | |

54. A VTVM, suitable for RF measurements and connected between plate and ground, is used to indicate resonance in a tank circuit acting as the plate load. The VTVM will show:
(a) a sharp rise as resonance is approached.
(b) a sharp dip as resonance is approached.
(c) zero reading at resonance.
(d) maximum reading equal to the B+ at resonance.
(e) a slow fall as resonance is approached, followed by a sharp rise.

(a) | | (b) | | (c) | | (d) | | (e) | |

55. When an audio amplifier contains distortion, the output waveform:
(a) cannot be improved by using negative feedback.
(b) possesses a number of harmonics.
(c) is still a faithful reproduction of the input signal.
(d) would contain only the original frequencies.
(e) Both (a) and (d) are true.

(a) | | (b) | | (c) | | (d) | | (e) | |

56. When a 110 V, 60 Hz source is connected across a coil of 13 ohms resistance, the current through the coil is 0.25 A. Find the coil's impedance.
(a) 10 ohms   (b) 13 ohms
(c) 780 ohms   (d) 440 ohms
(e) 130 ohms

(a) | | (b) | | (c) | | (d) | | (e) | |

57. Biasing the base of a PNP transistor moderately positive with respect to the emitter will:
(a) cause a punch-through of the base-emitter junction.
(b) reverse-bias the base-emitter junction.
(c) cause a large flow of majority carriers across the base-emitter junction.
(d) cause a large reverse current to flow across the collector-emitter junction.
(e) forward-bias the base-emitter junction.

(a) | | (b) | | (c) | | (d) | | (e) | |

58. A coil is designed to be tuned over the range of frequencies 500 to 1500 kHz. Its Q at 25 MHz will be:
(a) 25 times the value at 1 MHz.
(b) 5 times the value at 1 MHz.
(c) the same as at 1 MHz.
(d) lower than at 1 MHz, due to skin effect.

(e) able to provide excellent selectivity.

(a) I I   **(b)** I I   **(c)** I I   **(d)** I I   **(e)** I I

59. The moving-coil meter movement:
(a) operates on the generator principle.
(b) has a sensitivity which is always less than 1000 ohms per volt.
(c) does not respond to ac correctly.
(d) is rarely used in electronic measurements.
(e) is less sensitive than the hot wire movement.

(a) I I   **(b)** I I   **(c)** I I   **(d)** I I   **(e)** I I

60. The stage which feeds into a ratio detector in an FM receiver is the:
(a) frequency converter.
(b) local oscillator.
(c) BFO.
(d) audio amplifier.
(e) final IF amplifier, which also acts as a limiter.

(a) I I   **(b)** I I   **(c)** I I   **(d)** I I   **(e)** I I

61. The maximum forward bias which can safely be applied to the base-emitter junction is denoted by the maximum:
(a) emitter-to-ground voltage.
(b) emitter-collector voltage with the base grounded.
(c) emitter-to-base voltage.
(d) base-to-ground voltage.
(e) None of the above are true.

(a) I I   **(b)** I I   **(c)** I I   **(d)** I I   **(e)** I I

62. An FM deviation meter indicates:
(a) the peak voltage level reached by the FM signal.
(b) the maximum frequency shift of the FM signal away from the unmodulated carrier value.
(c) the average frequency shift of the FM signal away from the unmodulated carrier value.
(d) the maximum amount of unwanted drift in the unmodulated carrier frequency.
(e) the maximum value of the modulation index which occurs in the FM signal.

(a) I I   **(b)** I I   **(c)** I I   **(d)** I I   **(e)** I I

63. Which of the following is best for long distance FM communications?
(a) Wide band modulation systems.
(b) Narrow band modulation systems.
(c) A UHF carrier frequency rather than VHF.
(d) A minimum number of frequency multiplier stages in the transmitter.
(e) A single sideband FM transmitter.

(a) I I   **(b)** I I   **(c)** I I   **(d)** I I   **(e)** I I

64. For how much of the 360^0 signal cycle does the plate current flow in a class A RF voltage amplifier?

(a) 360^0 (b) 270^0 (c) 180^0
(d) 90^0 (e) 0^0

(a) I I   **(b)** I I   **(c)** I I   **(d)** I I   **(e)** I I

65. Standing waves:
(a) have a VSWR of 1.
(b) are caused by an impedance mismatch between the surge impedance of the line and the antenna load.
(c) produce no voltage nodes and antinodes on the line.
(d) decrease the losses on the transmission line.
(e) result in all the power traveling down the line being absorbed by the load.

(a) I I   **(b)** I I   **(c)** I I   **(d)** I I   **(e)** I I

66. If reverse bias is applied to a PN junction:
(a) electrons move toward the junction.
(b) the depletion region is unchanged.
(c) holes move toward the junction.
(d) the barrier region is decreased.
(e) the barrier region is increased.

(a) I I   **(b)** I I   **(c)** I I   **(d)** I I   **(e)** I I

67. In the circuit shown in Fig. 9, what is the output dc potential at point X with no-load conditions?
(a) +778 V   (b) -778 V   (c) +1100 V
(d) +1555 V   (e) -1555 V

(a) I I   **(b)** I I   **(c)** I I   **(d)** I I   **(e)** I I

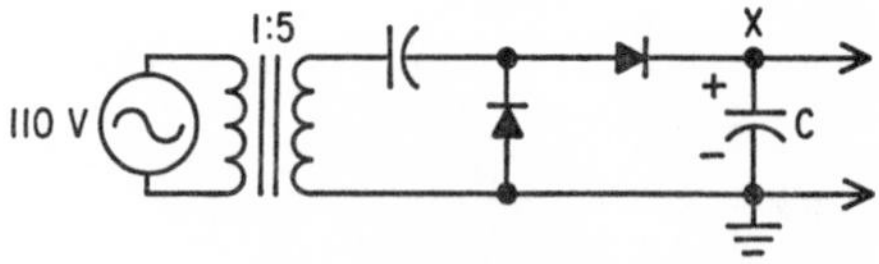

FIGURE 9

68. Two equal-value capacitors are each charged from a 200 V dc source. They are then connected in parallel with a third uncharged capacitor, also of the same value. What is the new voltage across the combination?
(a) 133 1/3 V   (b) 66 2/3 V
(c) 100 V   (d) 200 V
(e) 166 2/3 V

(a) I I   **(b)** I I   **(c)** I I   **(d)** I I   **(e)** I I

69. When a superheterodyne receiver is tuned to a strong signal, the delayed AVC bias is -2.5 V. The receiver is now re-tuned to pick up a very weak signal. The new AVC bias is:
(a) the same as before.
(b) more negative.
(c) less negative.
(d) slightly positive.
(e) zero.

(a) I I   **(b)** I I   **(c)** I I   **(d)** I I   **(e)** I I

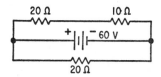

FIGURE 10

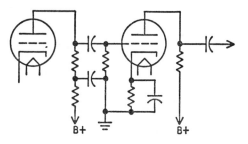

FIGURE 11

70. When all the flux lines created by the primary of a transformer link with the secondary, the coefficient of coupling between the two coils is:
(a) infinite   (b) 0   (c) 1   (d) 10
(e) -1

(a) | | (b) | | (c) | | (d) | | (e) | |

71. In the circuit shown in Fig. 10, what is the current drawn from the battery?
(a) 1.2 A   (b) 3.33 A   (c) 5 A
(d) 6.67 A   (e) 12 A

(a) | | (b) | | (c) | | (d) | | (e) | |

72. The cell case and terminals of a lead-acid storage cell may be cleaned with a solution of:
(a) baking soda and water.
(b) sulphuric acid.
(c) sal ammoniac and water.
(d) petroleum jelly.
(e) table salt and water.

(a) | | (b) | | (c) | | (d) | | (e) | |

73. The circuit shown in Fig. 11 illustrates:
(a) resistance-capacitance coupling.
(b) high resistance coupling.
(c) low impedance coupling.
(d) high impedance coupling.
(e) mutual coupling.

(a) | | (b) | | (c) | | (d) | | (e) | |

74. "Stacked arrays" result in the radiation being directed:
(a) at low vertical angles.
(b) at low horizontal angles.
(c) at medium and high vertical angles.
(d) at high vertical angles.
(e) omnidirectionally.

(a) | | (b) | | (c) | | (d) | | (e) | |

75. With a class C operated tetrode or pentode power amplifier, the cathode current is the sum of the:
(a) plate and screen grid currents.
(b) plate and control grid currents.
(c) plate, screen grid and control grid currents.
(d) plate, screen grid and suppressor grid currents.
(e) plate, control grid, screen grid and suppressor grid currents.

(a) | | (b) | | (c) | | (d) | | (e) | |

76. In the circuit shown in Fig. 12, what change(s) must be made for correct operation?
(a) D1 must be reversed.
(b) A capacitor must be connected between point A and ground.
(c) D2 must be reversed.
(d) C1 must be reversed.
(e) Both (c) and (d) are true.

(a) | | (b) | | (c) | | (d) | | (e) | |

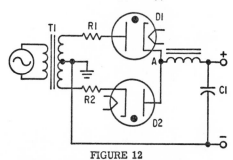

FIGURE 12

77. In a triode class B push-pull modulator:
(a) the average plate current during signal conditions is the same as the steady state current during no signal conditions.
(b) the average plate current fluctuates with the amplitude of the grid signal.
(c) the dc plate current flows continuously in each tube.
(d) the grid current flows for 160° of each cycle.
(e) the grid current flows for half of the input cycle.

(a) | | (b) | | (c) | | (d) | | (e) | |

78. The Q of a series resonant circuit determines:
(a) the voltage magnification.
(b) the sharpness of the response curve.
(c) the circuit's selectivity.
(d) the bandwidth.
(e) All of the above are true.

(a) | | (b) | | (c) | | (d) | | (e) | |

79. The voltage induced in a broadcast receiving antenna is determined by:

(a) the field strength at the antenna's position.
(b) the antenna's length.
(c) the angle between the antenna and the direction of the electric field.
(d) Only (a) and (b) are true.
(e) Not only (a) and (b) but (c) are true.

(a) I I   (b) I I   (c) I I   (d) I I   (e) I I

80. In Public Safety Radio Service stations operating below 470 MHz, the maximum permissible deviation permitted, using type F3 emission, is:
(a) $\pm$ 10 kHz   (b) $\pm$ 5 kHz   (c) $\pm$ 3 kHz
(d) $\pm$ 100 Hz   (e) $\pm$ 20 Hz

(a) I I   (b) I I   (c) I I   (d) I I   (e) I I

81. If the only dc source available is 120 V, what must be the value of a resistor, connected in series with a light bulb whose resistance is 100 ohms and is designed to work from a 12 V dc source?
(a) 900 ohms   (b) 100 ohms
(c) 90 ohms   (d) 11 ohms
(e) 1100 ohms

(a) I I   (b) I I   (c) I I   (d) I I   (e) I I

82. To check the state of charge in a lead-acid storage battery, you would use:
(a) a hydrometer.   (b) a wattmeter.
(c) a watt-hour meter.
(d) an ampere-hour meter.
(e) an ohmmeter.

(a) I I   (b) I I   (c) I I   (d) I I   (e) I I

83. A current of 0.15 A is flowing through a resistor of 100 ohms. Calculate the heat dissipation.
(a) 0.15 W   (b) 0.225 W   (c) 1.5 W
(d) 2.25 W   (e) 15 W

(a) I I   (b) I I   (c) I I   (d) I I   (e) I I

84. Regarding the schematic shown in Fig. 13, which of the following is a false statement?
(a) The circuit is a grounded collector stage.
(b) The circuit is an emitter follower.
(c) The circuit has a high input impedance and a low output impedance.
(d) The circuit has a low current gain but a high voltage gain.
(e) The output signal is in phase with the input signal.

(a) I I   (b) I I   (c) I I   (d) I I   (e) I I

85. In a communications receiver, which stages provide the most gain and selectivity?
(a) The RF amplifiers.   (b) The mixer.
(c) The IF amplifiers.   (d) The detector.
(e) The AF amplifiers.

(a) I I   (b) I I   (c) I I   (d) I I   (e) I I

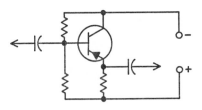

FIGURE 13

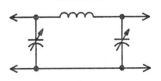

FIGURE 14

86. The circuit shown in Fig. 14 may be used:
(a) to attenuate harmonics.
(b) to generate harmonics.
(c) to attenuate sub-harmonics.
(d) as a high-pass filter.
(e) as a voltage doubling network.

(a) I I   (b) I I   (c) I I   (d) I I   (e) I I

87. In the circuit of Fig. 15, $R = X_L = X_C = 1$ kohm. If the source voltage is 100 V, what will a VTVM read when connected between B and D?
(a) 100 V   (b) 66 2/3 V   (c) 50 V
(d) 33 1/3 V   (e) 0 V

(a) I I   (b) I I   (c) I I   (d) I I   (e) I I

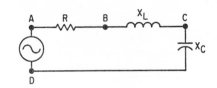

FIGURE 15

88. One advantage of push-pull operation over single-tube audio amplifiers is:
(a) the higher plate efficiency when class B is used.
(b) a greater power output.
(c) the cancellation of even harmonic distortion.
(d) no dc core saturation.
(e) All the above are true.

(a) I I   (b) I I   (c) I I   (d) I I   (e) I I

89. A buffer amplifier:
(a) is normally operated in class C.
(b) has a low input impedance.
(c) may be a common base stage.
(d) uses grid-leak bias.

(e) is used to prevent a reduction in an oscillator's frequency stability.

(a) I I   (b) I I   (c) I I   (d) I I   (e) I I

90. When making application for a new station license, who may not sign the application?
(a) An individual making the application.
(b) A responsible officer for a station to be operated by a company.
(c) A responsible appointed official for a local government station.
(d) A friend of an applicant who has a first-class license.
(e) The intended new manager of the station.

(a) I I   (b) I I   (c) I I   (d) I I   (e) I I

91. For class C operation, what changes, if any, are required in the circuit shown in Fig. 16?
(a) Reverse E1 battery polarity.
(b) Reverse both E1 and E2 battery polarities.
(c) Reverse E2 battery polarity.
(d) No changes are necessary.
(e) Remove E2 and provide a ground for the collector return.

(a) I I   (b) I I   (c) I I   (d) I I   (e) I I

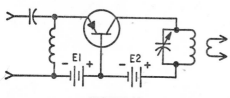

FIGURE 16

92. The Primary Frequency Standard on which highly accurate frequency measurements are based in the U.S.A. is maintained by:
(a) the National Bureau of Standards, Department of Commerce, in Boulder, Colo.
(b) the FCC in Washington, D.C.
(c) the National Bureau of Standards in New York City.
(d) the FCC in Hawaii.
(e) the National Bureau of Standards in Hawaii.

(a) I I   (b) I I   (c) I I   (d) I I   (e) I I

93. The FM broadcast system:
(a) is operated on a frequency band of 10 to 15 MHz.
(b) uses a narrower bandwidth than the AM standard broadcast system.
(c) uses a deviation ratio of less than 1.
(d) uses a receiver with an IF of 455 kHz.
(e) has a better signal to noise ratio than the AM standard broadcast system.

(a) I I   (b) I I   (c) I I   (d) I I   (e) I I

94. The VHF range includes the frequencies:
(a) 300 to 3,000 MHz
(b) 30,000 kHz to 300 MHz
(c) 3,000 to 30,000 kHz
(d) 300 to 3,000 kHz
(e) 30 to 3,000 kHz

(a) I I   (b) I I   (c) I I   (d) I I   (e) I I

95. A Pi network may act as:
(a) an impedance matching device.
(b) the tuned plate load of an amplifier.
(c) a low-pass filter to suppress harmonics.
(d) a means of efficiently transferring RF power.
(e) All the above are true.

(a) I I   (b) I I   (c) I I   (d) I I   (e) I I

96. The main disadvantage of a crystal oscillator is that:
(a) it is capable of generating only a single frequency.
(b) it has poor frequency stability.
(c) it has a low output.
(d) it has a low Q.
(e) it has a distorted output waveform.

(a) I I   (b) I I   (c) I I   (d) I I   (e) I I

97. You are observing an absorption wavemeter while it is resonant to the final output frequency of your transmitter. You notice that there is a dip in the meter's reading during modulation. This is known as:
(a) insufficient modulation.
(b) dynamic instability.
(c) transmitter intermodulation.
(d) positive carrier shift.
(e) negative carrier shift.

(a) I I   (b) I I   (c) I I   (d) I I   (e) I I

98. The resistance of a copper conductor:
(a) is reduced as the temperature rises.
(b) decreases when current flows through it.
(c) increases directly with the diameter of the conductor.
(d) increases at radio frequencies due to skin effect.

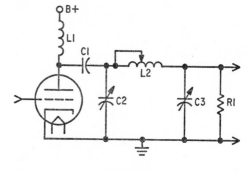

FIGURE 17

(e) decreases directly with an increase in
the conductor's length.

(a) I I   **(b)** I I   **(c)** I I   **(d)** I I   **(e)** I I

99. In the circuit shown in Fig. 17, which
component could be left out under normal operating conditions?
(a) C_1 (b) L_2 (c) C_2 (d) C_3
(e) R_1

(a) I I   **(b)** I I   **(c)** I I   **(d)** I I   **(e)** I I

100. A transmitter's third harmonic has a
heterodyne frequency meter reading of
2875.7. The calibration chart shows that
2875.0 corresponds to 1307.2 kHz, while
2876.0 corresponds to 1308.6 kHz. What is
the operating frequency of the transmitter?
(a) 436.06 kHz   (b) 435.86 kHz
(c) 1308.18 kHz   (d) 1307.46 kHz
(e) 1305.8 kHz

(a) I I   **(b)** I I   **(c)** I I   **(d)** I I   **(e)** I I

Element 3, Test 2

1. The circuit shown in Fig. 1 is not a frequency multiplier. C1 and C2 are included to provide:
(a) thermal stability.
(b) self bias.
(c) circuit resonance.
(d) a positive path of feedback voltage.
(e) neutralization.

(a) I I (b) I I (c) I I (d) I I (e) I I

2. What is the circuit shown in Fig. 1?
(a) An RF complementary push-pull circuit.
(b) An AF push-pull circuit.
(c) An RF push-pull circuit.
(d) An RF push-push circuit.
(e) An RF parallel circuit.

(a) I I (b) I I (c) I I (d) I I (e) I I

3. If an L of 1.25 H, a C of 15 μ f and an R of 130 ohms are connected in series, what is the resonant frequency?
(a) 37 Hz   (b) 370 Hz   (c) 74 kHz
(d) 740 kHz   (e) 74 Hz

(a) I I (b) I I (c) I I (d) I I (e) I I

4. The IF amplifier of a superheterodyne receiver is operated:
(a) class A.   (b) class AB.
(c) class B.   (d) class C.
(e) class D.

(a) I I (b) I I (c) I I (d) I I (e) I I

5. In the circuit shown in Fig. 2, what is the value of control grid bias?
(a) zero V   (b) -49 V   (c) -50 V
(d) -51 V   (e) -5 V

(a) I I (b) I I (c) I I (d) I I (e) I I

6. The magnitude of the emf induced in a conductor is governed by the:
(a) length of the conductor.
(b) speed with which the conductor is cutting the lines of force.
(c) angle at which the conductor is cutting the lines of force.
(d) flux density of the magnetic field.
(e) All of the above are true.

(a) I I (b) I I (c) I I (d) I I (e) I I

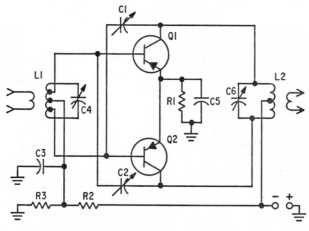

FIGURE 1

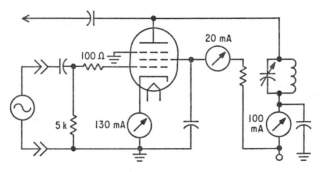

FIGURE 2

7. In the Public Safety Radio Services at frequencies between 50 and 450 MHz, the frequency tolerance for both fixed and base stations (authorized after 1961) is:
(a) 0.00002%   (b) 0.0001%
(c) 0.0005%   (d) 0.002%
(e) 0.001%

(a) I I   (b) I I   (c) I I   (d) I I   (e) I I

8. Two 10 μ F capacitors in series are fully charged from a 60 V dc source. The two capacitors are then disconnected from each other and from the source. They are then reconnected in parallel and placed across a third 10 μ F capacitor that was previously uncharged. What is the voltage across the third capacitor?
(a) 10 V   (b) 15 V   (c) 20 V
(d) 30 V   (e) 45 V

(a) I I   (b) I I   (c) I I   (d) I I   (e) I I

9. An audio transformer has a primary to secondary turns ratio of 5 to 1.
(a) If the primary load required is 1000 ohms, the transformer would provide a match for a 100 ohms secondary load.
(b) The transformer could be used as an inter-stage coupling between two vacuum tube audio voltage amplifiers.
(c) The transformer could be used to couple amplifiers with equal impedances.
(d) If the input voltage to the primary is 10 V, the secondary voltage is 50 V.
(e) None of the above are true.

(a) I I   (b) I I   (c) I I   (d) I I   (e) I I

10. In Public Radio Services, the width of the frequency band (normally specified in kilohertz) containing those frequencies upon which a total of 99% of the radiated power appears--extended to include any discrete frequency upon which the power is at least 0.25% of the total radiated power--is the:
(a) authorized bandwidth.
(b) carrier frequency.
(c) bandwidth occupied by an emission.

(d) sideband spectrum for television transmissions.
(e) None of the above are true.

(a) I I   (b) I I   (c) I I   (d) I I   (e) I I

11. The cloud of electrons between the control grid and the cathode is called the:
(a) ion cloud.
(b) space charge.
(c) Edison effect.
(d) molecular emission.
(e) secondary emission.

(a) I I   (b) I I   (c) I I   (d) I I   (e) I I

12. The primary purpose of adding a resistor in series with a voltmeter is to:
(a) decrease the voltage range.
(b) increase the voltage range.
(c) speed up the movement of the needle in order to take readings rapidly.
(d) dampen the movement of the needle to prevent overshoot.
(e) protect the meter movement against overload.

(a) I I   (b) I I   (c) I I   (d) I I   (e) I I

13. A circuit that could be used in conjunction with a detector to detect an A3J signal but not an A3 signal would be the:
(a) Foster-Seeley discriminator.
(b) ratio detector.
(c) stable beat frequency oscillator.
(d) delayed AVC circuit.
(e) "double-hump" tuned resonant circuit.

(a) I I   (b) I I   (c) I I   (d) I I   (e) I I

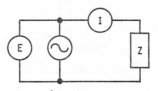

FIGURE 3

14. In the circuit shown in Fig. 3, the true power is given by:
(a) E x I   (b) I^2 x Z   (c) E^2/Z
(d) (E x I)/Power factor
(e) E x I x Power factor

(a) | | (b) | | (c) | | (d) | | (e) | |

15. Amplitude modulation created in a stage before the final RF power amplifier is called:
(a) direct modulation.
(b) indirect grid modulation.
(c) low level modulation.
(d) high level modulation.
(e) intermediate modulation.

(a) | | (b) | | (c) | | (d) | | (e) | |

16. When a transmitter has a low-pass filter connected between the transmitter output and the antenna, one reason it is used is to:
(a) attenuate the harmonic frequencies and spurious signals, while passing the desired carrier frequency to the antenna.
(b) increase the standing wave ratio.
(c) attenuate audio harmonics while passing the desired frequencies to the antenna.
(d) attenuate only the parasitic frequencies that are present in all transmitters.
(e) increase the standing waves on the transmission line.

(a) | | (b) | | (c) | | (d) | | (e) | |

17. If the full scale deflection current of a moving coil meter movement is 50 μ A, the meter sensitivity is:
(a) 50 Mohms   (b) 20 kohms
(c) 500 ohms per volt
(d) 20,000 ohms per volt
(e) 200 kohms per volt

(a) | | (b) | | (c) | | (d) | | (e) | |

18. If an AM superheterodyne receiver is tuned to receive 1,400 kHz and the local oscillator is producing 1,855 kHz, what signal frequency would cause image interference?
(a) 455 kHz   (b) 910 kHz   (c) 945 kHz
(d) 2310 kHz   (e) 2765 kHz

(a) | | (b) | | (c) | | (d) | | (e) | |

19. With regard to parasitic oscillations, which of the following is a false statement?
(a) Parasitic oscillations occur only in frequency multipliers.
(b) Parasitic oscillations may produce spurious sidebands.
(c) Parasitic oscillations consume power drawn from the B+ supply source.
(d) Parasitic oscillations may be generated by stray inductance, stray capacitance and positive feedback.
(e) Parasitic oscillations may be prevented by small resistors in series with the plate, control grid and screen grid.

(a) | | (b) | | (c) | | (d) | | (e) | |

20. An audio output transformer has a primary of 9000 turns and a secondary of 300 turns. If the secondary load is 4 ohms, what is the impedance of the primary?
(a) 120 ohms   (b) 0.133 ohms
(c) 3,600 ohms   (d) 36 kohms
(e) 1,200 ohms

(a) | | (b) | | (c) | | (d) | | (e) | |

21. Which of the following frequencies could be relied upon for long-distance communications using a high power transmitter using A1 emission?
(a) 20 kHz   (b) 100 kHz   (c) 200 kHz
(d) 20 MHz   (e) 200 MHz

(a) | | (b) | | (c) | | (d) | | (e) | |

22. The circuit diagram shown in Fig. 4 is:
(a) a series-fed Colpitts oscillator.
(b) a shunt-fed Colpitts oscillator.
(c) a tuned-grid, tuned-plate oscillator.
(d) an electron-coupled oscillator.
(e) a series-fed Hartley oscillator.

(a) | | (b) | | (c) | | (d) | | (e) | |

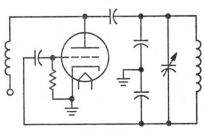

FIGURE 4

23. What system keeps an FM transmitter carrier frequency within tolerance, assuming that a reactance tube modulator is used?
(a) An AGC circuit.   (b) An AFC circuit.
(c) An AVC circuit.   (d) An ATC circuit.
(e) A DAVC circuit.

(a) | | (b) | | (c) | | (d) | | (e) | |

24. The high vacuum diode, when compared with a mercury vapor rectifier:
(a) is suitable for lower current power supplies.
(b) requires an extensive warm-up period.
(c) has a lower voltage drop when used with a choke input filter.
(d) requires no heater circuit.
(e) has a lower peak inverse voltage.

(a) | | (b) | | (c) | | (d) | | (e) | |

25. In a grounded base amplifier, when the input signal amplitude is increased, the signal voltage across the emitter-base junction will:
(a) increase.   (b) decrease.

(c) not change.   (d) reverse its phase.
(e) be zero.

(a) | | (b) | | (c) | | (d) | | (e) | |

26. For a particular heterodyne frequency meter, corresponding dial settings and frequencies are:

Dial Setting	Frequency
2553.8	1843 kHz
2558.4	1844 kHz

What is the frequency corresponding to a dial setting of 2556.0?
(a) 1843.478 kHz
(b) 1843.522 kHz
(c) 1842.522 kHz
(d) 1844.478 kHz
(e) 1843.956 kHz

(a) | | (b) | | (c) | | (d) | | (e) | |

27. What is the value and tolerance of a capacitor whose first row colors are (from left to right) white, brown, and red and whose second row colors are green, silver, and brown?
(a) 0.015 μ F $\pm$ 10%   (b) 1.2 μ F $\pm$ 5%
(c) 91 μ F $\pm$ 10%   (d) 91 $\mu\mu$ F $\pm$ 5%
(e) 120 $\mu\mu$ F $\pm$ 10%

(a) | | (b) | | (c) | | (d) | | (e) | |

28. For an electromagnetic wave to be successfully propagated in the $TE_{1,0}$ mode, the wider inside dimension of the waveguide must be:
(a) a full wavelength long.
(b) at least 1 1/2 wavelengths long.
(c) at least 1/4 wavelength long.
(d) at least 1/2 wavelength long.
(e) The wider dimension is not critical.

(a) | | (b) | | (c) | | (d) | | (e) | |

29. Coupling between a low impedance headphone and the plate output of a vacuum tube amplifier may be achieved by a:
(a) parallel capacitor.
(b) matching transformer.
(c) 1 to 1 transformer.
(d) parallel resistor.
(e) series inductor and a parallel capacitor.

(a) | | (b) | | (c) | | (d) | | (e) | |

30. Dynamotors are used to provide:
(a) grid bias voltage.
(b) dc filament voltage.
(c) ac cathode bias voltage.
(d) plate voltage.
(e) dc filtered voltages for crystal ovens.

(a) | | (b) | | (c) | | (d) | | (e) | |

31. A 500-W transmitter is amplitude modulated to 100% by a sinusoidal tone. The power in the lower sideband is:

(a) 125 W
(b) 250 W
(c) 500 W
(d) 62.5 W
(e) None of the above are true.

(a) | | (b) | | (c) | | (d) | | (e) | |

32. The physical length of a resonant Marconi antenna is:
(a) one quarter wavelength in free space.
(b) one-half wavelength in free space.
(c) 95% of one quarter wavelength in free space.
(d) 85% of one quarter wavelength in free space.
(e) 85% of one half wavelength in free space.

(a) | | (b) | | (c) | | (d) | | (e) | |

33. In the so-called klystron "drift space" between the cavity and the repeller:
(a) fast moving electrons are speeded up and slower moving electrons are retarded.
(b) fast moving electrons can catch up with the slower moving electrons.
(c) electrons are repelled back to the cathode.
(d) electron multiplication takes place.
(e) frequency multiplication takes place.

(a) | | (b) | | (c) | | (d) | | (e) | |

34. An antenna using a parasitic array:
(a) is omnidirectional.
(b) is unidirectional.
(c) is commonly used at VHF or UHF.
(d) has a low antenna gain.
(e) Both (b) and (c) are true.

(a) | | (b) | | (c) | | (d) | | (e) | |

35. Type approved equipment:
(a) means that the required data has been measured by FCC personnel.
(b) means that the equipment has been approved for any type of radio service.
(c) is subject to further data checking by the manufacturer.
(d) is based on data about a transmitter, submitted by the manufacturer.
(e) is only required for high powered base stations.

(a) | | (b) | | (c) | | (d) | | (e) | |

36. Motorboating in an audio amplifier stage can be caused by:
(a) a shorted filter capacitor in the power supply.
(b) an open-circuit plate decoupling resistor.
(c) an open plate decoupling capacitor.
(d) a shorted plate decoupling capacitor.
(e) Both (b) and (d) are true.

(a) | | (b) | | (c) | | (d) | | (e) | |

37. In a parallel tank circuit, the capacitive reactance is greater than the inductive reactance. The result is that the:
(a) source current lags the source voltage.
(b) source voltage leads the source current.
(c) circuit behaves capacitively.
(d) power factor is 0.
(e) Both (a) and (b) are true.

(a) I I   (b) I I   (c) I I   (d) I I   (e) I I

38. The state of charge of a dry cell battery can be determined by:
(a) using a hydrometer to measure the specific gravity of each cell. It should read 1.300 for a fully charged cell.
(b) measuring the output voltage with no load on the terminals. It should read 1.0 V.
(c) measuring its terminal voltage under normal load for that cell.
(d) measuring the voltage of each cell individually. The reading should be at least 2.5 V.
(e) using a watt-hour meter.

(a) I I   (b) I I   (c) I I   (d) I I   (e) I I

39. A meter that reads the energy consumed is:
(a) an ammeter.   (b) a wattmeter.
(c) a watt-hour meter.   (d) a voltmeter.
(e) a wavemeter.

(a) I I   (b) I I   (c) I I   (d) I I   (e) I I

40. A Faraday screen is used:
(a) to provide a low reluctance path.
(b) as an electrostatic shield.
(c) to shield a circuit from radar interference.
(d) to provide a low impedance path to ground.
(e) as a ferromagnetic screen.

(a) I I   (b) I I   (c) I I   (d) I I   (e) I I

41. Fixed bias in a class C operated RF power amplifier may be used:
(a) because the cathode bias is not large enough.
(b) to protect the tube if the input signal is too large.
(c) to limit the plate current if the drive from the previous stage fails.
(d) to limit the plate current before the following stages are tuned.
(e) Both (c) and (d) are true.

(a) I I   (b) I I   (c) I I   (d) I I   (e) I I

42. Type A3A emission is amplitude modulation for:
(a) telephony, single sideband, reduced carrier.
(b) telephony, double sideband.
(c) telephony, single sideband, suppressed carrier.

(d) telephony, with two independent sidebands.
(e) facsimile, with single sideband, reduced carrier.

(a) I I   (b) I I   (c) I I   (d) I I   (e) I I

43. If an absorption wavemeter is not very loosely coupled to the oscillatory circuit, the effect may be to:
(a) change the generated frequency slightly.
(b) detune the oscillatory circuit.
(c) overload the wavemeter.
(d) stop the circuit from oscillating.
(e) All the above are true.

(a) I I   (b) I I   (c) I I   (d) I I   (e) I I

44. One advantage of a pentode or beam power tube over a triode as an RF amplifier is:
(a) its lower input impedance.
(b) its lower power sensitivity.
(c) its lower noise output.
(d) that it does not require neutralizing.
(e) that it has no power loss in the plate circuit.

(a) I I   (b) I I   (c) I I   (d) I I   (e) I I

45. Advantages of a full-wave rectifier power supply over a half-wave rectifier power supply include:
(a) easier filtering.
(b) better regulation.
(c) longer life for the tubes.
(d) higher dc output voltage for a given transformer secondary voltage.
(e) Both (a) and (b) are true.

(a) I I   (b) I I   (c) I I   (d) I I   (e) I I

46. In the circuit shown in Fig. 5, what is the potential at the screen grid?
(a) +250 V   (b) +184 V   (c) +66 V
(d) +30 V   (e) +154 V

(a) I I   (b) I I   (c) I I   (d) I I   (e) I I

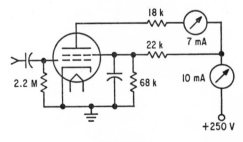

FIGURE 5

47. The surge impedance of a transmission line in ohms is approximately equal to:
(a) $\sqrt{L/C}$ (b) $\sqrt{C/L}$ (c) $\sqrt{L \times C}$
(d) $\sqrt{R \times G}$ (e) $\sqrt{L/CR}$

(a) I I   (b) I I   (c) I I   (d) I I   (e) I I

48. The capacitance of a capacitor may be increased by:
(a) decreasing the spacing between the plates.
(b) using an insulator with a higher dielectric constant.
(c) decreasing the area of the plates.
(d) reducing the applied voltage.
(e) Both (a) and (b) are true.

(a) I I   (b) I I   (c) I I   (d) I I   (e) I I

49. With a triode, a change of 3 V on the grid causes the plate current to change from 21 mA to 36 mA while the plate voltage remains constant at 150 V. What is the transconductance?
(a) 0.005 mho   (b) 7,000 μ mhos
(c) 12,000 μ, mhos   (d) 50,000 μ mhos
(e) 50 millimhos

(a) I I   (b) I I   (c) I I   (d) I I   (e) I I

50. An electric light bulb rated at 60 W will have consumed after 20 hours of use:
(a) 1.2 kW   (b) 80 W   (c) 12 kWh
(d) 0.8 kWh   (e) 1200 W–hr

(a) I I   (b) I I   (c) I I   (d) I I   (e) I I

51. A series ac circuit consists of a 150 μ.H coil, a 250 pF capacitor and a 12 kohm resistor. The source frequency is 820 kHz. What is the total impedance of the circuit?
(a) More than 20 kohms   (b) 18 kohms
(c) 15 kohms   (d) 12 kohms
(e) Less than 10 kohms

(a) I I   (b) I I   (c) I I   (d) I I   (e) I I

52. The output frequency of a crystal oscillator may be slightly changed by:
(a) connecting a capacitor across the crystal and its holder.
(b) connecting a capacitor across the plate tank circuit.
(c) making the grid leak resistor variable.
(d) connecting a low value resistor between the crystal and the grid.
(e) Both (a) and (b) are true.

(a) I I   (b) I I   (c) I I   (d) I I   (e) I I

53. An audio sine wave with a frequency of 2 kHz is used to frequency modulate an RF carrier. What is the frequency separation between adjacent sidebands?
(a) 2 kHz   (b) 1 kHz
(c) 4 kHz   (d) 6 kHz
(e) It depends on the frequency deviation.

(a) I I   (b) I I   (c) I I   (d) I I   (e) I I

54. If the RF carrier power is 1 kW and the modulating signal is a pure sine wave, what is the total power contained in the sidebands for 100% amplitude modulation?
(a) 125 W   (b) 250 W   (c) 500 W

(d) 750 W   (e) 1000 W

(a) I I   (b) I I   (c) I I   (d) I I   (e) I I

55. The schematic of Fig. 6 shows a two stage IF amplifier of an AM communications receiver. The circuit is operating correctly. The filaments of V1 and V2 are fed in parallel. S1 is in the CW position and the receiver has a 1 kHz bandwidth. While in the PHONE position, the receiver has a 10 kHz bandwidth. If the control grid potential of V2 is measured as a small negative voltage, which of the following is a possible cause?
(a) This is a normal condition for the control grid of V2, provided the signal is not weak.
(b) C4 is a short circuit.
(c) C7 is shorted.
(d) A short across the secondary of T1 will cause this condition.
(e) None of the above are true.

(a) I I   (b) I I   (c) I I   (d) I I   (e) I I

56. With reference to the schematic of Fig. 6, if the receiver is tuned to a telephony signal while S1 is in the CW position, which of the following would occur?
(a) The receiver would operate normally.
(b) The signal would be weak but undistorted.
(c) The signal would be badly distorted.
(d) The potential at the plate of V2 would be +250 V.
(e) The DAVC bias would fall to zero.

(a) I I   (b) I I   (c) I I   (d) I I   (e) I I

57. With reference to the schematic of Fig. 6, if the audio output from the loudspeaker increases while receiving a strong signal, which of the following is a possible cause?
(a) Capacitor C10 is shorted.
(b) Capacitor C7 is open.
(c) There is a short across R6.
(d) Capacitor C4 is shorted.
(e) Capacitor C6 is open.

(a) I I   (b) I I   (c) I I   (d) I I   (e) I I

58. In the schematic of Fig. 6, if C3 becomes open, which of the following would occur?
(a) The audio output from the loudspeaker would be zero.
(b) The plate current of V1 would rise.
(c) Resistor R4 might burn out.
(d) There would be an increased possibility of interstage oscillation.
(e) The dc potential at the plate of V1 would be +250 V.

(a) I I   (b) I I   (c) I I   (d) I I   (e) I I

59. In the schematic of Fig. 6, the receiver is tuned from a very strong CW station to a very weak CW station. Which of the following would occur?

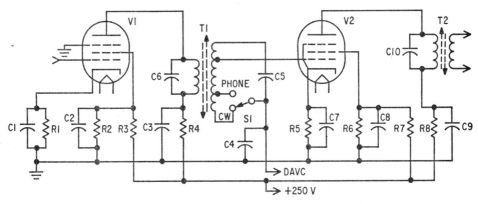

FIGURE 6

(a) The dc plate current of V1 would fall.
(b) The control grid potential of V2 would be zero.
(c) The dc screen current of V2 would fall.
(d) The cathode potential of V2 would be zero.
(e) Both (c) and (d) are true.

(a) I I   (b) I I   (c) I I   (d) I I   (e) I I

60. In the schematic of Fig. 6, if R2 becomes open, which of the following would occur?
(a) The cathode potential of V1 would decrease.
(b) The plate current of V1 would increase.
(c) The screen grid current of V1 would decrease.
(d) The screen grid potential of V1 would be +250 V.
(e) Both (a) and (c) are true.

(a) I I   (b) I I   (c) I I   (d) I I   (e) I I

61. In the schematic of Fig. 6, if the cathode potential of V2 is measured to be zero, which of the following is a possible cause?
(a) C10 is a short circuit.
(b) C9 is an open circuit.
(c) C8 is a short circuit.
(d) C7 is an open circuit.
(e) C5 is a short circuit.

(a) I I   (b) I I   (c) I I   (d) I I   (e) I I

62. With reference to the schematic of Fig. 6, which of the following would occur if the filament circuit of V1 is open?
(a) The dc potential of the plate of V1 is now zero volts.
(b) The cathode potential of V1 would be zero.
(c) The screen grid potential of V1 would be +250 V.
(d) The control grid potential of V2 would be slightly negative.

(e) Both (a) and (b) are true.

(a) I I   (b) I I   (c) I I   (d) I I   (e) I I

63. In the schematic of Fig. 6, the plate potential of V2 is measured at +250 V. Which of the following is a possible cause?
(a) An open circuit in the filament of V2.
(b) R6 is an open circuit.
(c) R5 is a short circuit.
(d) This is a normal condition.
(e) Both (a) and (b) are true.

(a) I I   (b) I I   (c) I I   (d) I I   (e) I I

64. With a signal present, C3 in the schematic of Fig. 6 becomes shorted. Which of the following would occur?
(a) The cathode potential of V2 would fall to zero.
(b) The screen grid current of V1 would fall to zero.
(c) The control grid potential of V2 would fall to zero.
(d) The plate potential of V1 would be +250 V.
(e) The screen grid potential of V1 would be +250 V.

(a) I I   (b) I I   (c) I I   (d) I I   (e) I I

65. When 360 V RMS exists between one end of a transformer secondary and its center tap, 120 V 60 Hz is applied to the primary of the power transformer. What is the turns ratio?
(a) 1 to 3   (b) 3 to 1   (c) 1 to 6
(d) 2 to 9   (e) 9 to 1

(a) I I   (b) I I   (c) I I   (d) I I   (e) I I

66. The schematic of Fig. 7 represents a class A amplifier circuit. For correct operation:
(a) A must be positive with respect to ground.
(b) A must be positive with respect to B.

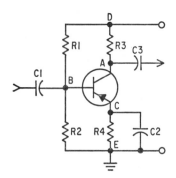

FIGURE 7

(c) B must be positive with respect to ground.
(d) B must be negative with respect to ground.
(e) C must be negative with respect to B.

(a) | | (b) | | (c) | | (d) | | (e) | |

67. Regarding the schematic of Fig. 7, which of the following is a false statement?
(a) The circuit is a common emitter amplifier.
(b) Point E must be positive with respect to point D.
(c) There is a 180° phase change between the input and output signals.
(d) The circuit has a current gain less than unity.
(e) The circuit has a high power gain.

(a) | | (b) | | (c) | | (d) | | (e) | |

68. With reference to the forward bias applied to the 400 mW transistor in the schematic of Fig. 7, which of the following statements is the most correct?
(a) The base and the emitter are maintained at the same potential.
(b) The base must be more than 1 V negative with respect to the emitter.
(c) With respect to the emitter, the base must be more than 1 V positive.
(d) With respect to the emitter, the base must be much less than 1 V positive.
(e) With respect to the emitter, the base must be less than 1 V negative.

(a) | | (b) | | (c) | | (d) | | (e) | |

69. The purpose of R1 and R2 in the schematic of Fig. 7 is to provide:
(a) forward bias for the base.
(b) the proper quiescent emitter bias for the transistor.
(c) the correct input impedance for the stage.
(d) a dc return path for the output of the stage.
(e) base and collector voltages that are equal to each other.

(a) | | (b) | | (c) | | (d) | | (e) | |

70. The purpose of R3 in the schematic of Fig. 7 is to provide:
(a) forward bias for the base-emitter junction.
(b) emitter bias (quiescent).
(c) a load impedance for the stage.
(d) a dc return path for the input current.
(e) temperature stability for the circuit.

(a) | | (b) | | (c) | | (d) | | (e) | |

71. To operate an NPN transistor properly in class A as an RF power amplifier, apply (with reference to ground) a:
(a) minus voltage to the emitter and minus voltage to the base.
(b) minus voltage to the base and positive voltage to the collector.
(c) positive voltage to the emitter and minus voltage to the base.
(d) minus voltage to the emitter and positive voltage to the base.
(e) Both (b) and (d) are true.

(a) | | (b) | | (c) | | (d) | | (e) | |

72. Three 12 V batteries each with an internal resistance of 0.3 ohms are connected in parallel. The combination has a total voltage of:
(a) 4 V and an internal resistance of 0.1 ohm.
(b) 12 V and an internal resistance of 0.3 ohm.
(c) 36 V and an internal resistance of 0.9 ohm.
(d) 12 V and an internal resistance of 0.1 ohm.
(e) 36 V and an internal resistance of 0.1 ohm.

(a) | | (b) | | (c) | | (d) | | (e) | |

73. If interstage transformer coupling is used between triode AF voltage amplifiers, the:
(a) transformer has a step-down ratio.
(b) frequency distortion is less than for RC coupling.
(c) transformer has a step-up ratio.
(d) phase distortion is less than for RC coupling.
(e) amplitude distortion is less than for RC coupling.

(a) | | (b) | | (c) | | (d) | | (e) | |

74. What is the total current drain from the source in the network shown in Fig. 8?
(a) 2.73 A   (b) 2.17 A   (c) 1.76 A
(d) 1.47 A   (e) 14.7 A

(a) | | (b) | | (c) | | (d) | | (e) | |

75. What may cause packing of the carbon granules in a carbon button microphone?
(a) Speaking close to the microphone in a loud voice.

(b) Connecting the microphone to the battery with the wrong polarity.
(c) Excessive current.
(d) Rapid temperature changes from 25° to 35°C.
(e) All of the above are true. This is the reason this microphone is not preferred for use with communications equipment.

(a) | | (b) | | (c) | | (d) | | (e) | |

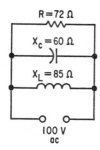

FIGURE 8

76. Pre-emphasis in an FM transmitter means:
(a) accentuating the higher modulating frequencies contained in an audio signal.
(b) accentuating the lower modulating frequencies contained in an audio signal.
(c) increasing the FM frequency deviation for the middle range of audio frequencies.
(d) increasing the FM deviation ratio to improve the signal-to-noise ratio at the receiver.
(e) increasing FM sideband power at the expense of carrier power to improve the signal-to-noise ratio at the receiver.

(a) | | (b) | | (c) | | (d) | | (e) | |

77. The greatest loss in a VHF matched co-axial line with air dielectric is the:
(a) copper loss.   (b) eddy-current loss.
(c) dielectric loss.   (d) radiation loss.
(e) hysteresis loss.

(a) | | (b) | | (c) | | (d) | | (e) | |

78. The part of the transmitted radio wave that is refracted back to earth is called the:
(a) indirect wave.   (b) direct wave.
(c) ground reflected wave.
(d) surface wave.   (e) space wave.

(a) | | (b) | | (c) | | (d) | | (e) | |

79. C2 in the circuit shown in Fig. 9 is an electrolytic capacitor. Which of the following statements is not correct?
(a) The circuit is a transistorized Colpitts oscillator.
(b) The function of R1 and R2 is to provide bias for the transistor base.

(c) A PNP transistor is used in this circuit. To use an NPN transistor, the only change necessary is to reverse the battery connections.
(d) The operating frequency of this circuit is determined primarily by the values of C3, C4 and L1.
(e) R3 cannot be by-passed with a capacitor.

(a) | | (b) | | (c) | | (d) | | (e) | |

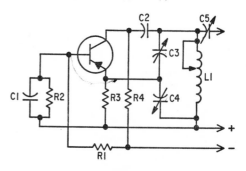

FIGURE 9

80. What is the percentage increase in antenna current in an AM transmitter when going from zero modulation to 90% modulation?
(a) 18.5%   (b) 22.5%   (c) 50%
(d) 33 1/3%   (e) 19.5%

(a) | | (b) | | (c) | | (d) | | (e) | |

81. What correction must be made to the discriminator circuit shown in Fig. 10?
(a) The diodes must be supplied with B+.
(b) C2 must be removed.
(c) C4 must be removed.
(d) D1 must be reversed.
(e) No corrections are necessary.

(a) | | (b) | | (c) | | (d) | | (e) | |

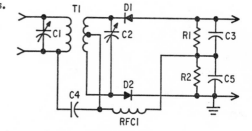

FIGURE 10

82. A reliable test to see whether a vacuum tube oscillator is working is to:
(a) measure the dc voltage across the grid leak resistor.
(b) measure the dc voltage on the screen grid.

(c) measure the dc voltage on the plate.
(d) monitor the screen voltage with an os-
    cilloscope.
(e) Both (b) and (c) above are true.

(a) | | (b) | | (c) | | (d) | | (e) | |

83. A 1 mH air-core inductor is wound with
a #15 copper wire. The wire is changed to a
#30 wire with the same number of turns, and
an iron core is inserted. The new inductance
will be:
(a) much less than 1 mH.   (b) 1/2 mH.
(c) much more than 1 mH.   (d) 1 mH.
(e) 1.1 mH.

(a) | | (b) | | (c) | | (d) | | (e) | |

84. The circuit shown in Fig. 11 is a:
(a) transistorized Hartley oscillator.
(b) transistor amplifier.
(c) Reinartz oscillator.
(d) transistorized Colpitts oscillator.
(e) transistorized Meissner oscillator.

(a) | | (b) | | (c) | | (d) | | (e) | |

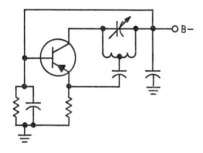

FIGURE 11

85. A piece of copper wire 40 ft long has a
resistance of 0.5 ohms per inch. If the diameter of the wire is halved, what is the new
value of the wire's total resistance?
(a) 48 ohms   (b) 96 ohms
(c) 480 ohms   (d) 960 ohms
(e) 2400 ohms

(a) | | (b) | | (c) | | (d) | | (e) | |

86. A class C stage can never be used for
audio frequency amplification because:
(a) the grid bias point is not on the transfer
    characteristic curve.
(b) grid current is allowed to flow.
(c) distortion in the output waveform is too
    severe.
(d) the plate current flows for less than half
    the cycle of the input signal.
(e) All the above are true.

(a) | | (b) | | (c) | | (d) | | (e) | |

87. Motor or generator commutators should
be cleaned and polished with:

(a) fine sand paper.   (b) a wire brush.
(c) graphite.   (d) fine emery paper.
(e) a fine file.

(a) | | (b) | | (c) | | (d) | | (e) | |

88. What is the bandwidth required for an
A3 type AM transmission using a 3 MHz
carrier and modulated by an audio signal
whose highest frequency is 5000 Hz?
(a) 3005 kHz   (b) 6010 kHz
(c) 5 kHz   (d) 10 kHz
(e) 2.5 kHz

(a) | | (b) | | (c) | | (d) | | (e) | |

89. A tuning stub may be compared with a:
(a) parallel LC circuit.
(b) series LC circuit.
(c) parallel CR circuit.
(d) series CR circuit.
(e) None of the above are true.

(a) | | (b) | | (c) | | (d) | | (e) | |

90. Magnetrons are useful as:
(a) amplifiers for broad-band microwave
    systems.
(b) microwave oscillators for low-power
    applications.
(c) high peak-power microwave generators.
(d) high peak-power microwave amplifiers.
(e) high peak-power microwave multipliers.

(a) | | (b) | | (c) | | (d) | | (e) | |

91. To cut off a thyratron after it has been
fired:
(a) the grid must be biased beyond cut off.
(b) no action is necessary. The tube will
    automatically de-ionize after a short
    time.
(c) the anode voltage must be reduced to
    zero.
(d) the anode voltage must be increased to
    the saturation point.
(e) a small negative pulse must be applied
    to the grid.

(a) | | (b) | | (c) | | (d) | | (e) | |

92. Under what circumstances will remote
control of a Public Safety Radio Services
transmitter, with the control point at a position other than the location of the transmitter, be authorized by the commission?
(a) When each transmitter shall be so in-
    stalled and protected that it is not acces-
    sible to or capable of operation by per-
    sons other than those duly authorized by
    the licensee.
(b) When equipment is installed to permit
    the person responsible for the operation
    of the transmitter to aurally monitor
    all transmissions originating at dis-
    patch points under his supervision.
(c) When facilities are installed which will
    permit the person responsible for the

operation of the transmitter either to disconnect the dispatch point circuits from the transmitter or to render the transmitter inoperative from any dispatch point under his supervision.
(d) When facilities are installed which will permit the person responsible for the operation of the transmitter to turn the transmitter carrier on and off at will.
(e) All the above are true.

(a) | | (b) | | (c) | | (d) | | (e) | |

93. The waveform shown in Fig. 12 indicates a percentage modulation of approximately:
(a) 0%   (b) 50%   (c) 100%   (d) 150%
(e) 200%

(a) | | (b) | | (c) | | (d) | | (e) | |

FIGURE 12

94. If the circuit current is divided by the source voltage, the result is the:
(a) reactance.   (b) impedance.
(c) resistance.   (d) acceptance.
(e) conductance.

(a) | | (b) | | (c) | | (d) | | (e) | |

95. With 100% AM plate modulation, the ratio of the peak value of the modulating voltage to the plate supply voltage of the RF modulated stage is:
(a) 10 to 1   (b) 1 to 10   (c) 2 to 1

(d) 1 to 2   (e) 1 to 1

(a) | | (b) | | (c) | | (d) | | (e) | |

96. To reduce the corrosion on the terminals of a battery, the terminals should first be cleaned and then coated with:
(a) a thin layer of H_2SO_4.
(b) a thin layer of petroleum jelly.
(c) a thin layer of sal ammoniac.
(d) a thin layer of potassium hydroxide.
(e) metallic paint.

(a) | | (b) | | (c) | | (d) | | (e) | |

97. A transmitter RF doubler stage is normally operated in:
(a) class D.   (b) class C.
(c) class B.   (d) class AB.
(e) class A.

(a) | | (b) | | (c) | | (d) | | (e) | |

98. Which of the following materials has the best insulating properties at radio frequencies?
(a) Mica.   (b) Parafin waxed paper.
(c) Oil.   (d) Wood.   (e) Glass.

(a) | | (b) | | (c) | | (d) | | (e) | |

99. For continuous long distance communications, which of the following frequencies are the most dependable?
(a) VLF.   (b) LF.   (c) MF.
(d) HF.   (e) VHF.

(a) | | (b) | | (c) | | (d) | | (e) | |

100. The eighth harmonic of a 2175 kHz fundamental frequency is:
(a) 1.74 MHz   (b) 174,000 kHz
(c) 17.4 MHz   (d) 1.74 GHz
(e) 2,183 kHz

(a) | | (b) | | (c) | | (d) | | (e) | |

Element 3, Test 3

1. When testing low-power transistors, it is advisable to set the ohmmeter range switch to:
(a) R x 1 (b) R x 10 (c) R x 100
(d) R x 1K (e) R x 10K

(a) | | (b) | | (c) | | (d) | | (e) | |

2. For class A operation in the schematic of Fig. 1, the:
(a) polarities of V1 and V2 are correct.
(b) polarity of V1 is reversed.
(c) polarity of V2 is reversed.
(d) polarities of both V1 and V2 are reversed.
(e) Nothing is wrong with the circuit.

(a) | | (b) | | (c) | | (d) | | (e) | |

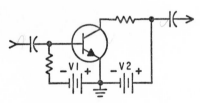

FIGURE 1

3. With reference to Fig. 1, it is assumed that the transistor is biased correctly. When the input signal goes positive, the:
(a) base becomes more negative with respect to the emitter.
(b) collector current flow increases.
(c) collector voltage becomes more positive.
(d) collector voltage becomes less positive.
(e) Both (b) and (d) above are true.

(a) | | (b) | | (c) | | (d) | | (e) | |

4. The universal emergency and distress frequency for aeronautical use is:
(a) 121.5 MHz   (b) 107 MHz
(c) 221.5 MHz   (d) 500 kHz
(e) 1.60 MHz

(a) | | (b) | | (c) | | (d) | | (e) | |

5. Rectification is achieved in a dc generator by using:
(a) a bridge rectifier. (b) a commutator.
(c) an alternator. (d) a silicon diode.
(e) a dynamotor.

(a) | | (b) | | (c) | | (d) | | (e) | |

6. A Marconi antenna is less than 1/4 wavelength long. If the antenna is end fed, the antenna load will be:
(a) inductive. (b) a high impedance.
(c) a low impedance. (d) capacitive.
(e) a low resistance.

(a) | | (b) | | (c) | | (d) | | (e) | |

7. The function of the limiter in an FM receiver is to:
(a) reduce adjacent channel interference.
(b) reduce image channel interference.
(c) eliminate all the frequency-modulated noise.
(d) remove all amplitude modulation from the signal.
(e) prevent loudspeaker blasting.

(a) | | (b) | | (c) | | (d) | | (e) | |

8. The harmonic content in the output of an RF power amplifier may be reduced by using:
(a) a lower Q tank circuit as the plate load.
(b) two tubes in parallel.
(c) two tubes in push-pull.
(d) a neutralizing circuit.
(e) class C operation.

(a) | | (b) | | (c) | | (d) | | (e) | |

9. A class B audio power amplifier must use an output transformer that:
(a) has a center-tapped primary.
(b) is designed to prevent core saturation caused by high dc current level in the primary.
(c) has a center-tapped secondary.
(d) is the load of a push-push arrangement.
(e) Both (b) and (d) are true.

(a) | | (b) | | (c) | | (d) | | (e) | |

10. When a VOM is switched to the 250 V dc scale, its total resistance is 5 Mohms. Its sensitivity is:
(a) 5 kohms per volt
(b) 20,000 ohms per volt
(c) 2,000 mhos
(d) 500 V per ohm
(e) 5,000 ohms per volt

(a) I I   (b) I I   (c) I I   (d) I I   (e) I I

11. A triode amplifier uses a tube with a μ of 30, and an r_p of 20 kohms. The plate supply voltage is 250 V, the grid bias is -8 V and the load resistor is 30,000 ohms. What is the voltage gain of the stage?
(a) 30   (b) 18   (c) 12   (d) 60
(e) 10

(a) I I   (b) I I   (c) I I   (d) I I   (e) I I

12. A power transformer has a primary of 1500 turns and a secondary of 500 turns. If the primary current is 6 A, what is the current supplied to the secondary load?
(a) 6 A   (b) 18 A   (c) 2 A   (d) 54 A
(e) 2/3 A

(a) I I   (b) I I   (c) I I   (d) I I   (e) I I

13. The ability of a resonant tank circuit to reduce the harmonic output of an RF power amplifier is mainly dependent upon its:
(a) cut-off frequency.
(b) being a series circuit.
(c) Q.
(d) operating frequency as determined by the formula, $f_r = 1/6.28 \sqrt{LC}$
(e) wide bandwidth.

(a) I I   (b) I I   (c) I I   (d) I I   (e) I I

14. If the length of a conductor is tripled and the diameter is halved, the new resistance will be:
(a) unchanged.   (b) 4 times as great.
(c) 6 times as great.   (d) 12 times as great.
(e) one-third of what it was.

(a) I I   (b) I I   (c) I I   (d) I I   (e) I I

15. In the push-pull pentode class A amplifier shown in Fig. 2, what (if anything) is wrong with the circuit?
(a) V2 and V3 are in push-pull, and therefore their grids must be driven 180° out of phase with each other by a phase inverter tube.
(b) C5 and C6 should be removed from the circuit and replaced with a conductor.
(c) C3 and C4 should be removed from the circuit and the connections should be left open.
(d) C3 and C4 should be removed from the circuit and replaced with a conductor.
(e) There is nothing wrong with the circuit, and it will operate without changes.

(a) I I   (b) I I   (c) I I   (d) I I   (e) I I

16. Raising the modulation percentage for an AM signal will produce:
(a) a reduction in the sideband power.
(b) a reduction in the carrier power if plate modulation is used.
(c) distortion if the modulation percentage exceeds 100%.
(d) improved signal-to-noise ratio at the input of the receiver, provided that the signal is not overmodulated.
(e) Both (c) and (d) are true.

(a) I I   (b) I I   (c) I I   (d) I I   (e) I I

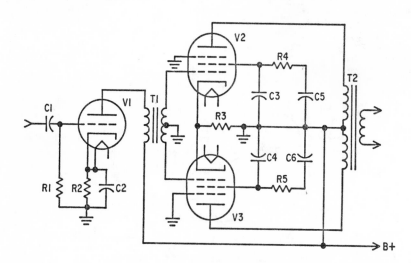

FIGURE 2

17. The mean power of Public Safety Radio Services emissions shall be attenuated below the mean output power of the transmitter on any frequency removed from the assigned frequency by more than 50 percent of, and up to and including 100 percent of, the authorized bandwidth, this attenuation, (in accordance with part 89 of the R&R's) being by at least:
(a) 20 dB   (b)   25 dB   (c) 10 dB
(d) 35 dB   (e)   80 dB

(a) I I   (b) I I   (c) I I   (d) I I   (e) I I

18. When a self-excited shunt wound generator is first started, the field current is generated as a result of the armature conductors cutting across the:
(a) permanent-magnet flux.
(b) residual flux.
(c) flux from an external source.
(d) same strength of flux that is used when the generator is running at full speed.
(e) reluctance in the field.

(a) I I   (b) I I   (c) I I   (d) I I   (e) I I

19. The period of a radio wave is 0.01 microseconds. What is its wavelength in free space?
(a) 0.03 m   (b)   30,000,000,000 m
(c) 0.3 m   (d)   0.03 km   (e) 3 m

(a) I I   (b) I I   (c) I I   (d) I I   (e) I I

20. What is a frequency converter tube?
(a) A tube used as an oscillator-mixer stage to conver the intermediate frequency to the audio frequency.
(b) An oscillator-mixer stage used to convert the radio frequency to an intermediate radio frequency.
(c) Either (a) or (b) is true.
(d) A tube that performs the functions of both oscillator and RF amplifier.

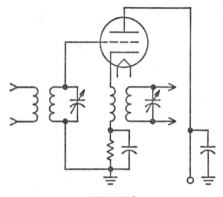

FIGURE 3

(e) A tube used for creating amplitude modulation.

(a) I I   (b) I I   (c) I I   (d) I I   (e) I I

21. The circuit shown in Fig. 3 represents:
(a) a phase splitter.
(b) an audio voltage amplifier.
(c) an audio limiter.
(d) a cathode follower.
(e) an audio power amplifier.

(a) I I   (b) I I   (c) I I   (d) I I   (e) I I

22. The circuit shown in Fig. 4 represents:
(a) an audio amplifier using two tubes in parallel.
(b) a push-pull amplifier.
(c) a phase inverter for a push-pull amplifier.
(d) a multivibrator.
(e) an RC phase shift oscillator.

(a) I I   (b) I I   (c) I I   (d) I I   (e) I I

23. The dc output voltage from a power supply has a no-load value of 115.5 V and a

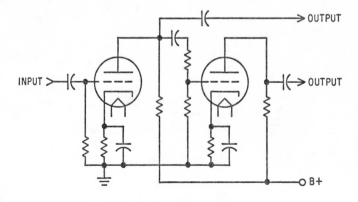

FIGURE 4

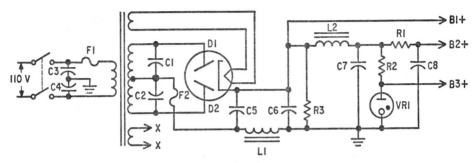

FIGURE 5

full-load value of 110 V. What is the percentage regulation?
(a) 5%　(b) 4.5%　(c) 95%　(d) 7.2%
(e) 9%

(a) |｜　(b) |｜　(c) |｜　(d) |｜　(e) |｜

24. Partition noise in a pentode amplifier tube is caused by the:
(a) random emission of electrons from the heated cathode.
(b) random division of the electron stream between the plate and control grid circuits.
(c) random division of the electron stream between the plate and screen grid circuits.
(d) random division of the electron stream between the screen grid and the suppressor grid circuits.
(e) secondary emission from the plate surface.

(a) |｜　(b) |｜　(c) |｜　(d) |｜　(e) |｜

25. The dielectric of a capacitor is changed from air to a material whose dielectric constant is 3. What will be the effect, if any, on the capacitive reactance, assuming that the frequency is unchanged?
(a) It will be increased 9 times.
(b) It will be divided by 3.
(c) There will be no change.
(d) It will be increased 3 times.
(e) It will be divided by 9.

(a) |｜　(b) |｜　(c) |｜　(d) |｜　(e) |｜

26. A 4700 ohm resistor is connected in series with a 1 H inductor across a 1 kHz source. What is the impedance of the circuit?
(a) 7844 ohms　　　(b) 6280 ohms
(c) 5753 ohms　　　(d) 1602 ohms
(e) 8370 ohms

(a) |｜　(b) |｜　(c) |｜　(d) |｜　(e) |｜

27. The capacitance of a capacitor may be increased by:
(a) decreasing the area of the plates.
(b) increasing the applied voltage.
(c) reducing the constant of the dielectric.
(d) increasing the spacing between the plates.
(e) reducing the thickness of the dielectric.

(a) |｜　(b) |｜　(c) |｜　(d) |｜　(e) |｜

28. A class C amplitude modulated RF amplifier uses grid leak bias only. If the filament of a previous stage burns out, then for this stage:
(a) the bias will increase and cut off the plate current.
(b) overmodulation will occur.
(c) the bias will go to zero.
(d) an excessive plate current will flow.
(e) Both (c) and (d) are true.

(a) |｜　(b) |｜　(c) |｜　(d) |｜　(e) |｜

29. The schematic of Fig. 5 shows the power supply circuit of a communications receiver. When the filament of the rectifier tube opens, which of the following results will not occur?
(a) The voltage at points B1+, B2+, and B3+ will all be zero.
(b) The voltage regulator tube will be extinguished.
(c) C5, C6, C7 and C8 will be completely discharged.
(d) The ac plate voltages of D1 and D2 will fall to zero.
(e) The dc voltage drop across L1 will be zero.

(a) |｜　(b) |｜　(c) |｜　(d) |｜　(e) |｜

30. In the schematic of Fig. 5, if the B1+ voltage falls to zero, which of the following is a possible cause?
(a) L2 is an open circuit.
(b) R1 is an open circuit.
(c) R2 is an open circuit.
(d) There is a short across L1.
(e) C6 is a short circuit.

(a) |｜　(b) |｜　(c) |｜　(d) |｜　(e) |｜

31. In the schematic of Fig. 5, if fuse F2 is blown, which of the following is not a possible cause?

(a) C7 is shorted.
(b) C5 is shorted.
(c) C8 is shorted.
(d) There is a short across L1.
(e) L2 is shorted to ground.

(a) | | (b) | | (c) | | (d) | | (e) | |

32. In the schematic of Fig. 5, if C5 is shorted, which of the following will not occur?
(a) B1+ will fall to zero.
(b) F2 will blow.
(c) The current through L2 will be zero.
(d) The secondary of the transformer will burn out.
(e) The voltage regulator tube will be extinguished.

(a) | | (b) | | (c) | | (d) | | (e) | |

33. In the schematic of Fig. 5, if C1 is open, which of the following will occur?
(a) Fuse F2 will blow.
(b) Fuse F1 will blow.
(c) The B1+ and B2+ voltages will fall to zero.
(d) Diode D1 will not conduct.
(e) An increased possibility of RF interference entering the receiver will exist.

(a) | | (b) | | (c) | | (d) | | (e) | |

34. If an AM transmitter has an unmodulated carrier power of 600 W and the percentage modulation is 80%, what is the power contained in the sidebands?
(a) 364 W   (b) 300 W   (c) 240 W
(d) 480 W   (e) 192 W

(a) | | (b) | | (c) | | (d) | | (e) | |

35. Broadcast logs containing entries of distress information or situations must be kept:
(a) until the radio station is sold.
(b) until the FCC authorizes the destruction of the logs.
(c) for 30 days.
(d) for 60 days.
(e) for one year.

(a) | | (b) | J   (c) | | (d) | | (e) | |

36. Stub-tuning does not:
(a) match impedances.
(b) eliminate parasitic oscillations.
(c) reduce standing waves.
(d) filter out odd harmonics.
(e) Both (b) and (d) are true.

(a) | | (b) | | (c) | | (d) | | (e) | |

37. What percentage increase in antenna current will occur when a carrier is 100% plate amplitude modulated?
(a) 12.25%   (b) 22.5%
(c) 50%   (d) 75%

(e) As with FM, the antenna current will not change during modulation.

(a) | | (b) | | (c) | | (d) | | (e) | |

38. Which of the following receivers contains an oscillator?
(a) Crystal receiver.
(b) Tuned radio frequency AM broadcast receiver.
(c) Superheterodyne receiver.
(d) Double conversion FM receiver.
(e) Both (c) and (d) are true.

(a) | | (b) | | (c) | | (d) | | (e) | |

39. With class C RF power amplifiers, a combination of cathode bias and grid-leak bias is frequently used to:
(a) reduce the level of input signal power required.
(b) increase the power output of the stage.
(c) increase the level of plate current before the previous stages are tuned.
(d) prevent an excessive level of plate current if the drive from the previous stage fails.
(e) increase the harmonic content of the output signal.

(a) | | (b) | | (c) | | (d) | | (e) | |

40. If a number of audio amplifiers use the same B+, the danger of motorboating may be reduced by:
(a) using a capacitor input filter.
(b) carefully filtering the B+.
(c) including RC decoupling networks in the plate circuits.
(d) increasing the values of the coupling capacitors.
(e) Both (c) and (d) are true.

(a) | | (b) | | (c) | | (d) | | (e) | |

41. A power supply uses a mercury vapor diode. This requires that:
(a) the plate voltage be applied before the filaments are heated.
(b) a capacitor input filter must always be used.
(c) a resistor capacitor filter must be used for good regulation.
(d) there be a warm-up period for the filaments before applying the plate voltage.
(e) Both (c) and (d) are true.

(a) | | (b) | | (c) | | (d) | | (e) | |

42. Excessive plate current in an amplifier circuit may be due to:
(a) loss of grid bias.
(b) an open circuit in the cathode bypass capacitor.
(c) inadequate filtering of the B+ supply.
(d) a shorted screen decoupling capacitor.
(e) poor regulation in the power supply.

(a) | | (b) | | (c) | | (d) | | (e) | |

43. The polarity of the field surrounding an electromagnet may be reversed by:
(a) reversing the position of the iron core.
(b) driving the core into saturation.
(c) demagnetizing the iron core by heat or vibration and then remagnetizing it.
(d) slowly increasing the current through the coil to a high value and then suddenly reducing it to zero.
(e) reversing the polarity of the source voltage and therefore changing the direction of current through the coil.

(a) I I   (b) I I   (c) I I   (d) I I   (e) I I

44. One quarter of an ac cycle represents:
(a) 0⁰   (b) 45⁰   (c) 90⁰   (d) 180⁰
(e) 270⁰

(a) I I   (b) I I   (c) I I   (d) I I   (e) I I

45. A unit used in the measurement of electrical energy is the:
(a) kWh   (b) kW   (c) coulomb
(d) kVA   (e) None of the above are true.

(a) I I   (b) I I   (c) I I   (d) I I   (e) I I

46. In troubleshooting transistor circuitry, we often use voltage measurements rather than resistance measurements because:
(a) the ohmmeter may become damaged.
(b) with the low values of resistance found in transistor circuitry, the readings would not be accurate enough.
(c) voltmeters are easier to use.
(d) the input resistance of the ohmmeter is too high.
(e) the current from the ohmmeter could damage the transistors.

(a) I I   (b) I I   (c) I I   (d) I I   (e) I I

47. The collector-to-base voltage (emitter open) rating of a transistor refers to the:
(a) maximum voltage between the collector and base of a transistor with the emitter open that can be used without danger of breakdown.
(b) maximum forward voltage that can be applied to a transistor's base with the emitter open.
(c) maximum forward collector current.
(d) minimum collector saturation voltage with the emitter open.
(e) None of the above are true.

(a) I I   (b) I I   (c) I I   (d) I I   (e) I I

48. In a frequency modulated transmitter, the number of sidebands:
(a) increases with the amplitude of the modulating signal.
(b) increases with a higher modulation index.
(c) decreases with an increase of the modulating frequency.
(d) increases with a higher degree of pre-emphasis.

(e) All of the above are true.

(a) I I   (b) I I   (c) I I   (d) I I   (e) I I

49. A traveling-wave tube has:
(a) an external electrostatic field.
(b) external electrostatic and electromagnetic fields.
(c) an external electromagnetic field.
(d) no external field.
(e) an element called the repeller.

(a) I I   (b) I I   (c) I I   (d) I I   (e) I I

50. A vertical quarter wave antenna would have to be 50 ft. long to resonate at the transmitted frequency. The only antenna available is 35 ft. long. The antenna could be made to resonate by:
(a) lowering the frequency.
(b) adding an inductor in series with the antenna.
(c) adding an LC circuit in parallel with the antenna.
(d) adding a capacitor in series with the antenna.
(e) Both (a) and (c) are true.

(a) I I   (b) I I   (c) I I   (d) I I   (e) I I

51. The IF stages of a superheterodyne receiver have been aligned. The next step would be the:
(a) alignment of the RF amplifier.
(b) alignment of the mixer stage.
(c) alignment of the local oscillator.
(d) alignment of the tuned circuit that is coupled to the antenna.
(e) Either (a) or (d) would be correct.

(a) I I   (b) I I   (c) I I   (d) I I   (e) I I

52. Neutralization is required in:
(a) push-pull RF circuits using triodes.
(b) push-push RF circuits using triodes.
(c) triode frequency multiplier stages.
(d) triode AF power amplifiers.
(e) RF amplifiers employing beam power tubes at low frequencies.

(a) I I   (b) I I   (c) I I   (d) I I   (e) I I

53. An amplifier has an output power of 5 W with an input signal power of 5 mW. The amplifier gain is:
(a) 55 dB   (b) 30 dB   (c) 25 dB
(d) 15 dB   (e) 5 dB

(a) I I   (b) I I   (c) I I   (d) I I   (e) I I

54. A moving-coil meter may be converted to a voltmeter by:
(a) adding a series multiplier resistor.
(b) adding a shunt resistor.
(c) adding a parallel multiplier resistor.
(d) adding a shunt inductor.
(e) by-passing the meter with a capacitor.

(a) I I   (b) I I   (c) I I   (d) I I   (e) I I

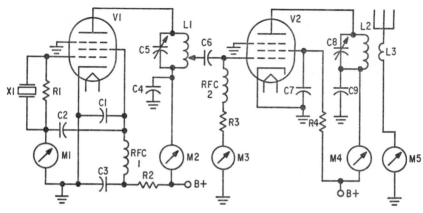

FIGURE 6

55. The true power in an ac circuit is 400 W. The source is 110 V, 60 Hz and the source current is 5 A. What is the power factor?
(a) 0.27   (b) 0.59   (c) 0.73
(d) 0.83   (e) 0.99

(a) || (b) || (c) || (d) || (e) ||

56. The inductance of a coil varies:
(a) as the square of the number of turns in the coil.
(b) inversely as the square of the coil's diameter.
(c) directly as the coil's diameter.
(d) directly as the number of turns in the coil.
(e) inversely as the square of the coil's length.

(a) || (b) || (c) || (d) || (e) ||

57. One picofarad is:
(a) 0.001 μ f   (b) 0.000001 μ F
(c) 0.0000001 μ F   (d) 0.0000000001 μ F
(e) 0.0001 μ F

(a) || (b) || (c) || (d) || (e) ||

58. The circuit shown in Fig. 6 is:
(a) Clapp crystal-controlled oscillator, coupled to a pentode power amplifier.
(b) Tri-tet crystal oscillator coupled to a pentode power amplifier.
(c) modified Pierce electron-coupled oscillator coupled to a pentode RF power amplifier.
(d) FM transmitter.
(e) tuned-grid tuned-plate oscillator, coupled to a tetrode power amplifier.

(a) || (b) || (c) || (d) || (e) ||

59. In the schematic of Fig. 6, if the tap on coil L1 were open:
(a) M1 and M2 would read low, and M4 would read high.

(b) M1, M2 and M3 would read low, and M4 would read high.
(c) M5 would read normal, and M4 would read high.
(d) M1 would read normal, and M3 and M5 would read zero.
(e) M4 and M2 would read high, and M5 and M3 would read low.

(a) || (b) || (c) || (d) || (e) ||

60. In the schematic of Fig. 6, if the crystal were removed from its socket while the power is applied:
(a) M1 and M2 would read zero, and M4 would read high.
(b) M2 and M4 would read high, and M3 would read zero.
(c) M3 would read low, and M4 and M5 would read high.
(d) M4 and M3 would read high, and M2 would read low.
(e) The circuit would self-oscillate.

(a) || (b) || (c) || (d) || (e) ||

61. In the schematic of Fig. 6, if the cathode connection were open on V2:
(a) M2 would read lower than normal, and M3, M4 and M5 would read zero.
(b) M1, M2 and M3 would read normal, and M4 and M5 would read zero.
(c) There would be no RF output, and M2 would read higher than normal.
(d) M2 and M4 would read higher than normal, and M3 would read zero.
(e) Excessive screen and plate current would flow in V2.

(a) || (b) || (c) || (d) || (e) ||

62. In a grounded collector circuit, the collector current is 5 mA and the base current is 100 μ A. The current gain is:
(a) 0.98   (b) 50   (c) 49   (d) 51
(e) 1.02

(a) || (b) || (c) || (d) || (e) ||

63. The number of significant sidebands in an FM signal will be increased with a:
(a) higher modulation index.
(b) lower frequency deviation ratio.
(c) reduced pre-emphasis.
(d) reduced RF power output.
(e) higher audio modulating frequency.

(a) I I   (b) I I   (c) I I   (d) I I   (e) I I

64. Which tube is dependent upon the electron transit time for its operation?
(a) Acorn tube.   (b) Lighthouse tube.
(c) Pentode tube.   (d) Klystron tube.
(e) Mercury vapor tube.

(a) I I   (b) I I   (c) I I   (d) I I   (e) I I

65. For the electrolyte, a lead-acid cell uses:
(a) potassium hydroxide.
(b) sulphuric acid and water.
(c) sal ammoniac and water.
(d) pure distilled water.
(e) lead sulphate.

(a) I I   (b) I I   (c) I I   (d) I I   (e) I I

66. At a distance of one mile from a transmitter, the field strength is 400 millivolts per meter. If the transmitter power is tripled, what is the distance from the transmitter to the 200 millivolt per meter contour?
(a) 18 miles   (b) 6 miles
(c) 3.5 miles   (d) 2.83 miles
(e) 1.5 miles

(a) I I   (b) I I   (c) I I   (d) I I   (e) I I

67. One difference between push-pull and push-push stages is that in:
(a) push-pull, grids are fed 180º out of phase, while in push-push, they are in phase.
(b) push-pull, the grids are fed in phase, while in push-push, they are 180º out of phase.
(c) push-pull, the load is connected between the plates, while in push-push, the plates are connected to one end of the load.
(d) push-push, the load is connected between the plates, while in push-pull, the plates are connected together to one end of the load.
(e) None of the above are true.

(a) I I   (b) I I   (c) I I   (d) I I   (e) I I

68. A cathode follower tube circuit, employed at audio frequencies:
(a) uses positive feedback.
(b) uses negative feedback.
(c) uses no feedback.
(d) matches a low impedance source to a high impedance load.
(e) is equivalent to a common emitter amplifier.

(a) I I   (b) I I   (c) I I   (d) I I   (e) I I

69. The circuit shown in Fig. 7 is a:
(a) series-fed Colpitts oscillator.
(b) shunt-fed Colpitts oscillator.
(c) tuned-grid tuned-plate oscillator.
(d) series-fed Hartley oscillator.
(e) shunt-fed Hartley oscillator.

(a) I I   (b) I I   (c) I I   (d) I I   (e) I I

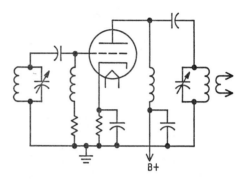

FIGURE 7

70. The output voltage of a rectifier circuit is stabilized by a VR tube. The series current-limiting resistor becomes an open circuit. What would be the effect on the regulated output voltage?
(a) The current through the VR tube would increase sharply, the tube would then burn out, and the output voltage would fall to zero.
(b) The output voltage would remain the same.
(c) The output voltage would increase.
(d) The output voltage would decrease.
(e) The output voltage would fall to zero.

(a) I I   (b) I I   (c) I I   (d) I I   (e) I I

71. The circuit shown in Fig. 8:
(a) is a common-base circuit.
(b) has too much forward bias applied between the base-emitter junction.
(c) has too much reverse bias applied to the base-collector junction.
(d) is a common collector circuit.
(e) uses an NPN transistor.

(a) I I   (b) I I   (c) I I   (d) I I   (e) I I

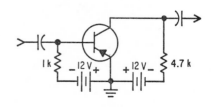

FIGURE 8

72. In an ac circuit, the reactance of a fixed capacitor decreases from 1 kohm to 200 ohms. How has the frequency changed?
(a) The frequency is five times its original value.
(b) The frequency is one-fifth of its original value.
(c) The frequency is unchanged since capacitive reactance does not depend on the frequency.
(d) The frequency is 25 times its original value.
(e) The frequency is 15 times its original value.

(a) I I   (b) I I   (c) I I   (d) I I   (e) I I

73. Three 10 V cells each with an internal resistance of 0.1 ohms are connected in series-aiding. The combination has a total voltage and a total internal resistance of:
(a) 30 V and 0.3 ohm.
(b) 30 V and 0.1 ohm.
(c) 10 V and 0.3 ohm.
(d) 10 V and 0.1 ohm.
(e) 30 V and 0.033 ohm.

(a) I I   (b) I I   (c) I I   (d) I I   (e) I I

74. In a transistorized Colpitts oscillator, the feedback voltage to the base occurs:
(a) through the collector-base junction capacitance.
(b) through the base-emitter junction capacitance.
(c) through the emitter-collector capacitance.
(d) across one capacitor of the feedback capacitive voltage divider in parallel with the tank coil.
(e) by means of a tap on the plate tank coil.

(a) I I   (b) I I   (c) I I   (d) I I   (e) I I

75. The emitter resistor of a common-emitter stage is often by-passed with a capacitor to:
(a) maintain the collector current at a safe value for changes in the transistor.
(b) decrease distortion and increase the frequency response of the stage.
(c) maintain the stage gain by preventing degeneration that would be caused if the emitter resistor were not by-passed.
(d) allow a smaller value of emitter resistor to be used.
(e) increase the static current of the collector and therefore increase the stage current gain.

(a) I I   (b) I I   (c) I I   (d) I I   (e) I I

76. The ratio of the input audio power to the input dc power required for 100% sinusoidal plate modulation of the final transmitter stage is:
(a) 1 to 1   (b) 2 to 1
(c) 1 to 2   (d) more than 2 to 1

(e) less than 1 to 2

(a) I I   (b) I I   (c) I I   (d) I I   (e) I I

77. Frequency modulation telephony is referred to as what type of emission?
(a) A0   (b) F0   (c) F1   (d) F2
(e) F3

(a) I I   (b) I I   (c) I I   (d) I I   (e) I I

78. The negative plate of a primary cell is constructed of:
(a) iron oxide.   (b) zinc.
(c) nickel hydrate.   (d) carbon.
(e) lead.

(a) I I   (b) I I   (c) I I   (d) I I   (e) I I

79. If a thin quarter-wave antenna that is resonant and matched to its transmission line at 1 MHz is operated at 1200 kHz, the antenna will:
(a) behave capacitively.
(b) behave inductively.
(c) behave as a resistive load of greater than 35 ohms.
(d) transmit more power than when it is operated at 1 MHz.
(e) still be matched to the transmission line.

(a) I I   (b) I I   (c) I I   (d) I I   (e) I I

80. To ground communications equipment aboard ships at sea, you would preferably use a:
(a) thin round copper wire connected to the deck of the vessel.
(b) thin wide flat copper strap connected to the metal deck of the vessel.
(c) thin solid copper wire connected to the mast of the vessel.
(d) thin stranded copper wire connected to the mast of the vessel.
(e) number of thin copper wires which form a ground plane by being attached to the deck of the vessel.

(a) I I   (b) I I   (c) I I   (d) I I   (e) I I

81. The schematic shown in Fig. 9 is an RCA Speaker/Amplifier assembly used for UHF communications in the 450 to 470 MHz range. In what class of operation are 52Q1 and 52Q2 being used?
(a) Class C.   (b) Class B.
(c) Class AB or class B.   (d) Class A.
(e) None of the above.

(a) I I   (b) I I   (c) I I   (d) I I   (e) I I

82. In the schematic of Fig. 9, the purpose of thermistor 52RT1 is to:
(a) attenuate the input signal.
(b) reduce the forward bias current of 52Q1 and 52Q2 as temperature increases.
(c) reduce harmonic distortion in the signal crossover.

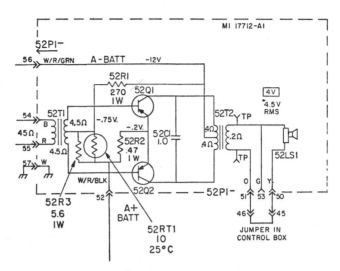

FIGURE 9   (Courtesy, RCA Corporation)

(d) produce relatively constant audio output
     regardless of audio input.
(e) limit the low frequency response of the
     amplifier.

(a) | | (b) | | (c) | | (d) | | (e) | |

83. In the schematic of Fig. 9, with normal
audio signal input, there is no signal output.
A possible cause is that:
(a) 52Q1 collector is open internally.
(b) 52Q2 collector is open internally.
(c) 52R3 has a short across it.
(d) 52R1 is open.
(e) 52R2 is open.

(a) | | (b) | | (c) | | (d) | | (e) | |

84. In the schematic of Fig. 9, an excessive
amount of distortion in the audio output is not
caused by:
(a) 52R1 being open.
(b) a small mismatch of 52Q1 and 52Q2.
(c) 52C1 being shorted.
(d) 52R2 being open.
(e) Any of the above.

(a) | | (b) | | (c) | | (d) | | (e) | |

85. In an ac series circuit, the resistance is
330 ohms, the inductive reactance is 835
ohms and the capacitive reactance is 505
ohms. What is the phase relationship between the source voltage and the current?
(a) Resonance exists and therefore the vol-
     tage and current are in phase.
(b) The voltage leads the current by 90°.
(c) The voltage lags the current by 90°.
(d) The current lags the voltage by 45°.
(e) The current leads the voltage by 45°.

(a) | | (b) | | (c) | | (d) | | (e) | |

86. In a dc circuit, if the power and the re-

sistance are known, the voltage may be
found by:
(a) $E = P/I$ (b) $E = P/R$
(c) $E = \sqrt{P/R}$ (d) $E = \sqrt{R/P}$
(e) $E = \sqrt{P \times R}$

(a) | | (b) | | (c) | | (d) | | (e) | |

87. If the by-pass capacitor in the plate circuit of the audio amplifier shown in Fig. 10
has a short circuit:
(a) the plate current would increase.
(b) motor-boating might occur.
(c) the amplifier output would increase.
(d) the tube would be damaged.
(e) the plate voltage would fall to zero.

(a) | | (b) | | (c) | | (d) | | (e) | |

88. A transistor has one emitter, one base
and one collector. Two connections are made
to the base, one to the emitter and one to the
collector. This transistor is called a:
(a) unijunction transistor.
(b) tetrode transistor.   (c) mixer.

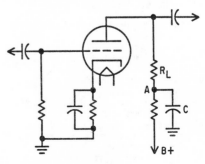

FIGURE 10

(d) converter.   (e) full wave rectifier.

(a) I I   (b) I I   (c) I I   (d) I I   (e) I I

89. When matching the plate circuit of a tube
to a transmission line and a Marconi antenna
with a pi-network, which of the following
statements is not true?
(a) The coupling efficiency is 100% and
     there will be no loss of energy.
(b) The pi-network is used to match the
     high plate impedance of the tube to the
     low impedance of the transmission line
     and the antenna.
(c) The loss of energy due to standing waves
     is minimized.
(d) The even harmonic power output is re-
     duced.
(e) The odd harmonic power output is re-
     duced.

(a) I I   (b) I I   (c) I I   (d) I I   (e) I I

90. The base of a transistor is often compared to what element of a vacuum tube?
(a) The plate of the vacuum tube.
(b) The cathode of the vacuum tube.
(c) The suppressor grid of the vacuum tube.
(d) The control grid of the vacuum tube.
(e) The screen grid of the vacuum tube.

(a) I I   (b) I I   (c) I I   (d) I I   (e) I I

91. An advantage of link coupling is:
(a) its minimum transfer of energy.
(b) an increase in the bandwidth of the cir-
     cuit using link coupling.
(c) its capability of being used at very low
     frequencies.
(d) a reduction in the transfer of harmonic
     energy.
(e) Both (a) and (b) are true.

(a) I I   (b) I I   (c) I I   (d) I I   (e) I I

92. The largest angle at which a sky wave
can penetrate the ionosphere and still be refracted back to earth is called the:
(a) angle of refraction.
(b) angle of reflection.
(c) angle of incidence.
(d) maximum ionospheric angle.
(e) critical angle.

(a) I I   (b) I I   (c) I I   (d) I I   (e) I I

93. Comparing the properties of grid and
plate modulation:
(a) with grid modulation, the power in the
     transmitted sidebands is supplied by the
     modulator.
(b) grid modulation produces less distor-
     tion at 100% modulation.
(c) with plate modulation, the audio power
     requirement is greater.
(d) grid modulation is more desirable in
     high-power broadcast transmitters at
     100% modulation.
(e) Both (a) and (b) are true.

(a) I I   (b) I I   (c) I I   (d) I I   (e) I I

94. Assuming that the lowest frequency in-
volved is 50 Hz, what would be a typical
value for a capacitor to bypass a cathode
resistor of 2.2 kohms?
(a) 50 μ F   (b) 25 μ F   (c) 15 μ F
(d) 5 μ F   (e) 0.05 μ F

(a) I I   (b) I I   (c) I I   (d) I I   (e) I I

95. A quartz crystal used in an oscillator
circuit functions by virtue of:
(a) magnetostriction.
(b) electrostriction.
(c) piezoelectric effect.
(d) degenerative feedback.
(e) mechanical feedback.

(a) I I   (b) I I   (c) I I   (d) I I   (e) I I

96. 110 V, 60 Hz is applied to the primary
of a transformer with a 1 to 10 step-up
ratio and a center-tapped secondary. Under
no-load conditions, what is the voltage
across the input filter capacitor of a full-
wave rectifier?
(a) 1100 V   (b) 778 V   (c) 550 V
(d) 389 V   (e) 887 V

(a) I I   (b) I I   (c) I I   (d) I I   (e) I I

97. If the source frequency is 60 Hz, the
ripple frequency in the output of a three-
phase half-wave rectifier circuit is:
(a) 350 Hz   (b) 180 Hz   (c) 120 Hz
(d) 60 Hz   (e) 30 Hz

(a) I I   (b) I I   (c) I I   (d) I I   (e) I I

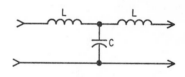

FIGURE 11

98. The circuit shown in Fig. 11 is a:
(a) high-pass filter.   (b) low-pass filter.
(c) band-pass filter.   (d) band-stop filter
(e) M-derived section.

(a) I I   (b) I I   (c) I I   (d) I I   (e) I I

99. The unit of conductance is the:
(a) coulomb.   (b) erg.   (c) ohm.
(d) farad.   (e) mho.

(a) I I   (b) I I   (c) I I   (d) I I   (e) I I

100. Keeping the grid voltage at -4 V, a
change of 5 V in the plate voltage produces
a change of 0.5 mA in the plate current. The
ac plate resistance is:
(a) 1 kohm   (b) 5 kohms
(c) 10 kohms   (d) 25 kohms
(e) 1 millimho.

(a) I I   (b) I I   (c) I I   (d) I I   (e) I I

Element 3, Test 4

1. What is the value of a resistor that is color coded yellow, violet and yellow?
(a) 474 ohms. (b) 4.7 kohms.
(c) 47 kohms. (d) 4700 kohms.
(e) 0.47 Mohms.

(a) | | (b) | | (c) | | (d) | | (e) | |

2. If a coil is drawing a current of 1.5 A from a 90 V, 60 Hz supply, the impedance of the coil is:
(a) 135 ohms. (b) 50 ohms.
(c) 60 ohms. (d) 1590 ohms.
(e) The problem cannot be solved from the information given.

(a) | | (b) | | (c) | | (d) | | (e) | |

3. The phase difference between the input signal on the grid and the output signal from the plate of a resistance-loaded amplifier is:
(a) 0º (b) +90º (c) -90º (d) 180º
(e) 360º

(a) | | (b) | | (c) | | (d) | | (e) | |

4. An amplifier is biased to provide class A operation so that plate current is flowing throughout the cycle of the applied signal. For what part of the 360º cycle does grid current flow?
(a) 90º (b) 30º to 45º (c) 0º
(d) 180º (e) 360º

(a) | | (b) | | (c) | | (d) | | (e) | |

5. A terminated rhombic antenna:
(a) is used for long distance communications.
(b) is unidirectional.
(c) directs the main radiation lobe at a certain angle towards the ionosphere.
(d) is one form of a long-wire directive array.
(e) All the above are true.

(a) | | (b) | | (c) | | (d) | | (e) | |

6. The speed regulation of a motor, in percentage, is equal to:

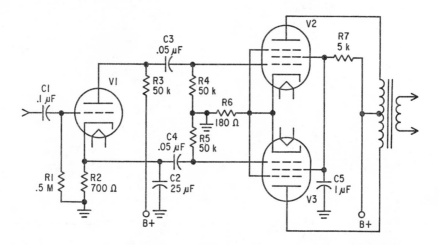

FIGURE 1

(a) the ratio of the full-load speed to the difference between the full-load and no-load speeds.
(b) the full-load speed over the no-load speed.
(c) the no-load speed over the full-load speed.
(d) the difference between the no-load and full-load speeds, divided by the full-load speed and multiplied by 100.
(e) the ratio of the difference between the full-load and no-load speeds to the no-load speed.

(a) I I   (b) I I   (c) I I   (d) I I   (e) I I

7. What changes (if any) are required for the circuit shown in Fig. 1 to function properly as a class A push-pull audio amplifier?
(a) V2 and V3 screen grids must have separate screen dropping resistors and individual by-pass capacitors to ground.
(b) C2 must be removed.
(c) R2 and R3 must have approximately equal values.
(d) R4 must be much larger than R5 to compensate for the gain of V1.
(e) Both (b) and (c) are correct.

(a) I I   (b) I I   (c) I I   (d) I I   (e) I I

8. The schematic of Fig. 2 represents a class A amplifier circuit. For correct operation:
(a) A must be positive with respect to ground.
(b) A must be positive with respect to B.
(c) B must be positive with respect to ground.
(d) B must be negative with respect to ground.
(e) C must be negative with respect to B.

(a) I I   (b) I I   (c) I I   (d) I I   (e) I I

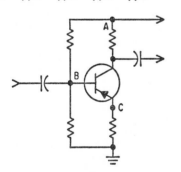

FIGURE 2

9. The current drawn from a 110 V, 60 Hz source is 6 A, and the cosine of the phase angle between the voltage and the current is 0.45. What is the power consumption in the circuit?

(a) 0.66 kW   (b) 297 W   (c) 328 W
(d) 542 W   (e) 1.47 kW

(a) I I   (b) I I   (c) I I   (d) I I   (e) I I

10. The schematic shown in Fig. 3 is an RCA 1st oscillator-multiplier circuit used in a UHF communications receiver, for intended use in the 450 MHz to 470 MHz range. The function of 14R19 is to:
(a) provide a dc current path from 14Q1 collector to A- supply voltage.
(b) broaden the frequency response of the tank circuit, 14L11 and 14C21, for the four oscillator frequencies.
(c) reduce the signal amplitude at the collector of 14Q5.
(d) Both (a) and (b) are true.
(e) Both (b) and (c) are true.

(a) I I   (b) I I   (c) I I   (d) I I   (e) I I

11. In the schematic of Fig. 3, with the frequency selector in the position shown, the dc voltage at terminal 14 is zero and not normal. Which defect will not cause this effect?
(a) 14R1 is open.   (b) 14R2 is open.
(c) 14R8 is open.   (d) 14L3 is open.
(e) 14C2 is open.

(a) I I   (b) I I   (c) I I   (d) I I   (e) I I

12. In the schematic of Fig. 3, there is no multiplier output signal, and terminal 25 is at zero volts dc and not normal. Terminal 14 signal is dc negative and normal. What is a possible cause for this condition?
(a) There is a short across 14R26.
(b) 14L13 is open.
(c) There is a short across 14R27.
(d) There is a short across 14R33
(e) None of the above are true.

(a) I I   (b) I I   (c) I I   (d) I I   (e) I I

13. In the schematic of Fig. 3, there is no oscillator signal and the voltage at terminal 14 is zero. Which of the following conditions is not a possible cause?
(a) 14C2 is open.
(b) 14R2 is open.
(c) 14R22 has a short across it.
(d) 14L3 is open.
(e) 14R3 has a short across it.

(a) I I   (b) I I   (c) I I   (d) I I   (e) I I

14. In the schematic of Fig. 3, the purpose (s) of capacitors 14C25 and 14C26 is to provide a:
(a) low impedance drive for the base of 14Q6.
(b) part of the resonant circuit of the collector of 14Q5.
(c) high impedance drive for the base of 14Q6.
(d) voltage divider to provide bias for 14Q6.

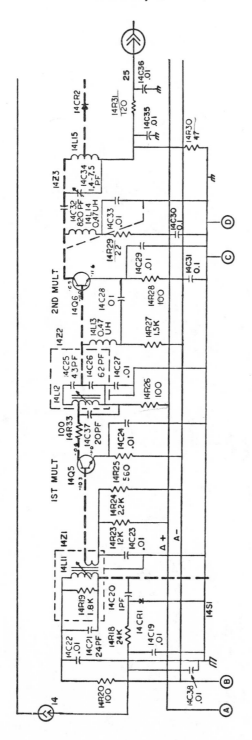

FIGURE 3 (continued on p. 38)
(Courtesy, RCA Corporation)

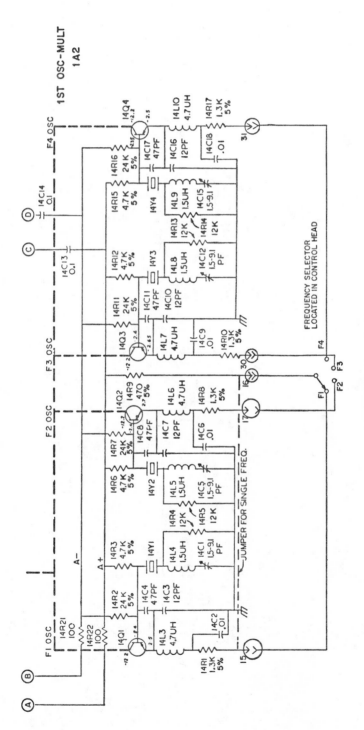

FIGURE 3 (continued)

(Courtesy, RCA Corporation)

(e) Both (a) and (b) are true.

(a) | | (b) | | (c) | | (d) | | (e) | |

15. How many measurements are required for a complete check of a transistor, using an ohmmeter?
(a) Two.   (b) Three.   (c) Four.
(d) Six.   (e) Eight.

(a) | | (b) | | (c) | | (d) | | (e) | |

16. In a common-emitter AF amplifier using fixed-bias the:
(a) input and output signal voltages are 90° out of phase.
(b) emitter-collector junction is forward biased.
(c) input and output signals are 180° out of phase.
(d) collector current decreases when the base current increases.
(e) base-emitter junction is reverse biased.

(a) | | (b) | | (c) | | (d) | | (e) | |

17. Which of the following is the least adequate as an insulator at UHF?
(a) Bakelite.   (b) Ceramics.
(c) Teflon.   (d) Mica.
(e) Polystyrene.

(a) | | (b) | | (c) | | (d) | | (e) | |

18. In the circuit shown in Fig. 4, the transformer has a primary to full secondary turns ratio of 1 to 2. What is the output voltage across C with no load?
(a) 220 V   (b) 311 V   (c) 440 V
(d) 622 V   (e) 110 V

(a) | | (b) | | (c) | | (d) | | (e) | |

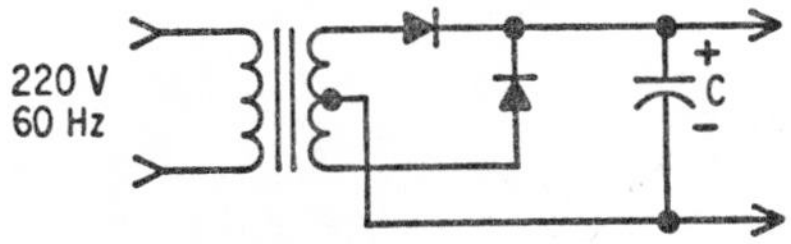

220 V
60 Hz

FIGURE 4

19. The power output of a transmitter is doubled. By what factor will the field strength be multiplied at a distance of one mile from the transmitter?
(a) 2.0   (b) 4.0   (c) 1.414
(d) 2.282   (e) 1.5

(a) | | (b) | | (c) | | (d) | | (e) | |

20. Facsimile by direct frequency modulation of the carrier is denoted by what symbol?
(a) F5   (b) F1   (c) F2
(d) F0   (e) F4

(a) | | (b) | | (c) | | (d) | | (e) | |

21. If it has a high deviation ratio, the main advantage of an FM communications system over an AM system is:

(a) better communication over long distances.
(b) a narrower bandwidth.
(c) the greater reduction of noise in the receiver output.
(d) a wider tolerance allowed in the stability of the carrier frequency.
(e) that the receiver alignment is less critical.

(a) | | (b) | | (c) | | (d) | | (e) | |

22. A unit of electrical energy is the:
(a) watt.   (b) kilowatt.   (c) watt-hour.
(d) coulomb.   (e) horsepower.

(a) | | (b) | | (c) | | (d) | | (e) | |

23. The current drawn from a 60 Hz source is 7.3 A. The circuit consists of 23 ohms of capacitive reactance, 10 ohms of inductive reactance and 13 ohms of resistance in series. What is the phase angle?
(a) 85°   (b) 45°   (c) 55°   (d) 75°
(e) 25°

(a) | | (b) | | (c) | | (d) | | (e) | |

24. In amplitude modulation, sidebands:
(a) contain the intelligence contained in the AM wave.
(b) are created by the effect of the audio signal on the RF carrier in the modulated stage.
(c) represent undesirable distortion of the carrier wave.
(d) are the audio frequencies contained in the AM wave.
(e) Both (a) and (b) are true.

(a) | | (b) | | (c) | | (d) | | (e) | |

25. In one type of voltage doubler circuit,
(a) a duo-triode is commonly used.
(b) a center tapped secondary is necessary.
(c) the two filter capacitors are connected in series across the load to produce the output voltage.
(d) silicon rectifiers are essential.
(e) Both (b) and (c) are true.

(a) | | (b) | | (c) | | (d) | | (e) | |

26. Cathode bias by itself cannot provide class C operation because:
(a) if class "C" bias were to be provided only by cathode bias, no plate current could flow, for the tube would have to be biased beyond plate current cut-off.
(b) the power dissipation in the cathode resistor would be excessive.
(c) the regenerative feedback across the cathode resistor would be too great.
(d) with a large voltage drop across the cathode resistor, the plate voltage would have to be increased to an impractical value.
(e) with no grid current flowing, the signal

bias would be much greater than that provided by the cathode resistor.

(a) I I   (b) I I   (c) I I   (d) I I   (e) I I

27. A beat frequency oscillator:
(a) is used to detect telephony.
(b) is used to make audible the presence of a telegraphy CW signal.
(c) is a crystal oscillator contained within a tuned radio frequency (TRF) receiver.
(d) produces an audio output from the loudspeaker when its output is mixed with the local oscillator frequency.
(e) Both (b) and (d) are true.

(a) I I   (b) I I   (c) I I   (d) I I   (e) I I

28. Due to a mismatch between a transmission line and its load, one quarter of the incident power is reflected from the load back along the line. The VSWR on the line is:
(a) 0   (b) 1   (c) 2   (d) 3   (e) 4

(a) I I   (b) I I   (c) I I   (d) I I   (e) I I

29. A determination of a radio station's operating frequency is made by comparison with the signals from station:
(a) WWV of the Federal Communications Commission.
(b) WWV of the National Bureau of Standards.
(c) WKW of Washington, D.C.
(d) WWW of the National Frequency Control Authority.
(e) WKW of the National Bureau of Standards.

(a) I I   (b) I I   (c) I I   (d) I I   (e) I I

30. The waveform shown in Fig. 5 represents:
(a) an unmodulated RF carrier.
(b) an AM wave.
(c) an FM wave.
(d) a PDM wave.
(e) Either (c) or (d) is correct.

(a) I I   (b) I I   (c) I I   (d) I I   (e) I I

31. It is required to measure the power drawn from the power supply. Using only a voltmeter in the circuit shown in Fig. 6, this can be calculated from:
(a) $V^2_{AB}/100$ k
(b) $V_{AC}^2/100$ k
(c) $(V_{AB} \times V_{BC})/100$ k
(d) $(V_{AC} \times V_{AB})/100$ k
(e) $(V_{AB} + V_{BC})^2/100$ k

(a) I I   (b) I I   (c) I I   (d) I I   (e) I I

32. 220V, 60Hz is applied to the primary of a power transformer. The primary current is 1 amp and the secondary current is 2 amps. What is the secondary voltage?
(a) 880 V   (b) 440 V   (c) 220 V

FIGURE 5

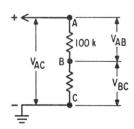

FIGURE 6

(d) 55 V   (e) 110 V

(a) I I   (b) I I   (c) I I   (d) I I   (e) I I

33. What should be the approximate value of a grid resistor that can provide contact bias?
(a) 100 kohms.   (b) 470 kohms.
(c) 680 kohms.   (d) 300 kohms.
(e) Over 2 Mohms.

(a) I I   (b) I I   (c) I I   (d) I I   (e) I I

34. A gain of 40 dB is equivalent to a:
(a) power ratio of 10^4.
(b) power ratio of 10^{-4}.
(c) voltage ratio of 10^4.
(d) voltage ratio of 10^{-4}.
(e) current ratio of 10^4.

(a) I I   (b) I I   (c) I I   (d) I I   (e) I I

35. The function of an FM limiter stage is to:
(a) prevent any amplitude modulation from being applied to the discriminator.
(b) produce the same effect as the noise limiter in an AM receiver.
(c) prevent the audio output increasing to an excessively high level.
(d) provide a means of detection for the FM signal.
(e) limit the intermediate frequency bandwidth.

(a) I I   (b) I I   (c) I I   (d) I I   (e) I I

36. Which instrument measures a frequency by beating it with a known frequency that may be varied until a zero beat occurs?
(a) An absorption wavemeter.
(b) A digital frequency meter.
(c) A grid dip meter.
(d) A heterodyne frequency meter.
(e) A calibration frequency meter.

(a) I I   (b) I I   (c) I I   (d) I I   (e) I I

37. When viewing the wave-shape with an oscilloscope in the circuit shown in Fig. 7, an approximate sawtooth wave shape would appear between points:
(a) B and C.   (b) A and B.
(c) B and D.   (d) C and D.
(e) None of the above, for the circuit will not produce sawtooth waves.

(a) | | (b) | | (c) | | (d) | | (e) | |

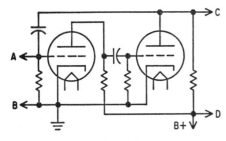

FIGURE 7

38. A good practice to follow while tuning a transmitter that has never been previously tuned is to:
(a) first tune the oscillator, couple the antenna and resonate the final amplifier tank circuit.
(b) apply protective bias to the oscillator.
(c) use an absorption wave meter and tune all stages (approximately) before power is applied.
(d) use a grid-dip meter and tune all stages to resonance before power is applied.
(e) check for the presence of parasitics.

(a) | | (b) | | (c) | | (d) | | (e) | |

39. The circuit shown in Fig. 8 is:
(a) a high-pass filter.
(b) a low-pass filter.
(c) a band-pass filter.
(d) a band-stop filter.
(e) an M-derived filter.

(a) | | (b) | | (c) | | (d) | | (e) | |

40. A full-wave rectifier circuit:
(a) requires two diodes.
(b) changes dc into fluctuating ac.
(c) requires the use of one diode and no transformer.
(d) must not be used with a choke input filter.
(e) has poor regulation compared with the half-wave circuit.

(a) | | (b) | | (c) | | (d) | | (e) | |

41. Regarding the temperature coefficient of a crystal, which of the following statements is false?
(a) With a positive temperature coefficient, the crystal frequency increases as the temperature increases.

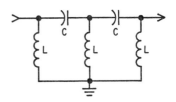

FIGURE 8

(b) With a negative temperature coefficient, the crystal frequency decreases as the temperature increases.
(c) Temperature coefficients may either be positive or negative.
(d) For some crystals, there is a particular temperature at which the coefficient is zero.
(e) A crystal has a frequency of 10 MHz. When the temperature increases by 20°C, the frequency is 9.999.97 kHz. The positive temperature coefficient equals 1.25 Hz per MHz per °C.

(a) | | (b) | | (c) | | (d) | | (e) | |

42. An RF amplifier may be operated linear class B rather than class C in order to:
(a) amplify an AM wave.
(b) generate odd harmonics only.
(c) cancel even harmonics.
(d) increase the plate efficiency.
(e) increase the harmonic content in the output signal.

(a) | | (b) | | (c) | | (d) | | (e) | |·

43. The load represented by a resonant rhombic antenna used for long distance fixed service communication is:
(a) 35 ohms.   (b) 73 ohms.
(c) 320 ohms.   (d) 600 ohms.
(e) dependent upon the wavelength of the transmitted wave and the length of each leg and the angle formed at the feed point of the antenna.

(a) | | (b) | | (c) | | (d) | | (e) | |

44. Citizens Radio Service is:
(a) a personal or business radio service.
(b) an amateur radio service.
(c) part of the Public Safety Radio Service.
(d) part of the Business Radio Service.
(e) None of the above is true.

(a) | | (b) | | (c) | | (d) | | (e) | |

45. While servicing an FM transmitter, the oscillator tube is found to be defective. What steps should be taken to place the transmitter back into service?
(a) Replace the oscillator tube, tune the transmitter, and then measure the final output frequency.
(b) Replace the damaged tube and put it back on the air.

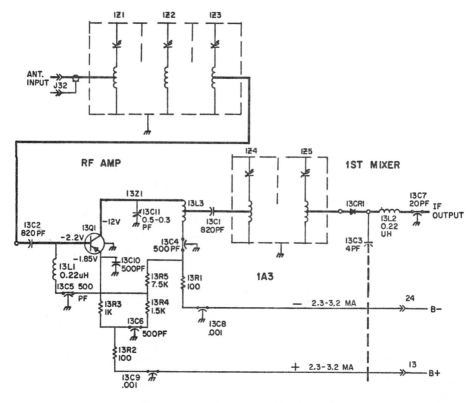

FIGURE 9 (Courtesy, RCA Corporation)

(c) First determine what caused the oscilla-tor tube to fail and then replace the tube.

(d) Replace the oscillator tube, tune the oscillator and check its frequency. Check the tuning of the rest of the trans-mitter using a dummy load, check the output frequency, and then place the transmitter back on the air.

(e) Replace the tube and record this inform-ation in the log.

(a) | | (b) | | (c) | | (d) | | (e) | |

46. The schematic shown in Fig. 9 is an RF amplifier and the 1st mixer stage. It is used in an RCA communications receiver for use on the 450 to 470 MHz band. The unit does not use a grounded power supply, and the voltages shown are in reference to the B+ terminal. If capacitor 13C10 is open, which of the following will occur?

(a) The emitter voltage will decrease.

(b) Thermal instability will increase.

(c) An increase in the regenerative feedback may lead to self-oscillations.

(d) The forward bias on the emitter-base junction will increase.

(e) The RF signal input to the first mixer will decrease.

(a) | | (b) | | (c) | | (d) | | (e) | |

47. In the schematic of Fig. 9, which com-ponents provide neutralization of the RF am-plifier?

(a) 13L1   (b) 13C5

(c) 13R5 and 13R4   (d) 13C11

(e) The stage is not neutralized.

(a) | | (b) | | (c) | | (d) | | (e) | |

48. In the schematic of Fig. 9, the collector current is measured and found to be high and increasing. The base voltage is approximate ly normal. Which of the following is a possi-ble cause?

(a) 13C2 is an open circuit.

(b) 13L3 has a short across it.

(c) 13R2 is an open circuit.

(d) 13C11 is an open circuit.

(e) 13R3 has a short across it.

(a) | | (b) | | (c) | | (d) | | (e) | |

49. In the schematic of Fig. 9, the RF vol-tage, while being monitored at the collector,

suddenly vanishes. Which of the following is a possible cause?
(a) 13C11 is shorted.
(b) 13C4 has changed slightly in value.
(c) 13R1 has a short circuit across it.
(d) 13R4 has increased in value slightly.
(e) 13C10 is open.

(a) | | (b) | | (c) | | (d) | | (e) | |

50. In the schematic of Fig. 9, the output from the 1st mixer is zero while receiving a strong signal. Which of the following is a possible cause?
(a) 13L2 has a short across it.
(b) 13C11 is an open circuit.
(c) 13C6 is an open circuit.
(d) 13R3 is an open circuit.
(e) 13R1 has a short across it.

(a) | | (b) | | (c) | | (d) | | (e) | |

51. The base voltage is measured and is appreciably more negative than the value indicated on the schematic of Fig. 9. Which of the following is a possible cause?
(a) The receiver is picking up a strong signal.
(b) 13R4 is an open circuit.
(c) 13C11 is an open circuit.
(d) 13R5 is an open circuit.
(e) 13R3 has a short across it.

(a) | | (b) | | (c) | | (d) | | (e) | |

52. The coulomb is the basic unit of:
(a) charge.   (b) capacitance.
(c) work.   (d) power.
(e) reactance.

(a) | | (b) | | (c) | | (d) | | (e) | |

53. In the circuit shown in Fig. 10, if the frequency is increased:

(a) the output voltage may either increase or decrease according to whether the frequency is above or below resonance.
(b) the voltage across the load will decrease.
(c) the voltage across the load will increase.
(d) the voltage across resistor R1 will decrease.
(e) you cannot tell whether the output voltage will increase or decrease without knowing the component values.

(a) | | (b) | | (c) | | (d) | | (e) | |

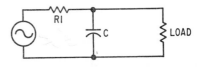

FIGURE 10

54. In the circuit shown in Fig. 11, what is the bias voltage?
(a) -33 V   (b) +33 V   (c) -22 V
(d) +367 V   (e) +400 V

(a) | | (b) | | (c) | | (d) | | (e) | |

55. The internally generated sawtooth waveform in a cathode ray oscilloscope is used to provide:
(a) vertical deflection.
(b) horizontal deflection.   (c) brightness.
(d) focus.   (e) sync.

(a) | | (b) | | (c) | | (d) | | (e) | |

56. A tripler stage:
(a) has an RF power output that is three times the input power.
(b) uses a plate tank circuit tuned to the third harmonic of the input signal frequency.

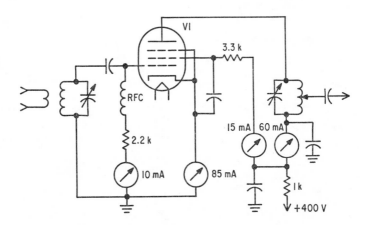

FIGURE 11

(c) has an output impedance that is three times the input impedance.
(d) can use a push-push arrangement.
(e) may use class B operation for highest efficiency.

(a) I I   (b) I I   (c) I I   (d) I I   (e) I I

57. The electric and magnetic fields waves which are radiated from an antenna are:
(a) 90° out of time phase, 90° apart in space, and at 90° to the direction of propagation.
(b) 90° out of time phase but 90° apart in space and at 45° to the direction of propagation.
(c) 180° out of time phase but 45° apart in space and at 90° to the direction of propagation.
(d) in time phase but 90° apart in space and at 45° to the direction of propagation.
(e) None of the above are true.

(a) I I   (b) I I   (c) I I   (d) I I   (e) I I

58. For amplification in the traveling wave tube, the power that is added to the wave is obtained from the:
(a) helix line.   (b) control grid.
(c) input resonant cavity.
(d) electron beam.   (e) collector plate.

(a) I I   (b) I I   (c) I I   (d) I I   (e) I I

59. The forward resistance of an emitter base junction is measured as 200 ohms. The reverse resistance should be:
(a) 200 ohms.   (b) 2 kohms.
(c) greater than 20 kohms.   (d) 400 ohms.
(e) 5000 ohms.

(a) I I   (b) I I   (c) I I   (d) I I   (e) I I

60. An NPN audio amplifier in the common base configuration has both the emitter-base and collector-base junctions forward biased. Which statement is true?
(a) This is a normal condition for amplification.
(b) A decrease in collector current will be observed.
(c) The transistor will not amplify the input signal.
(d) The collector is positive with respect to the base.
(e) The emitter-base junction resistance will be maximum.

(a) I I   (b) I I   (c) I I   (d) I I   (e) I I

61. A load draws a 9 A current from three 12 V batteries that are connected in series-aiding. The conductance of the load is:
(a) 4 ohms.   (b) 0.75 mho.
(c) 108 W   (d) 0.25 mho.
(e) 1.33 ohms.

(a) I I   (b) I I   (c) I I   (d) I I   (e) I I

62. Three capacitors of 6 μ F, 3 μ F and 2 μ F are connected in series. What is the total capacitance of the combination?
(a) 11 μ F   (b) 1 μ F
(c) 1.5 μ F   (d) 2 μ F
(e) The problem cannot be solved unless the frequency is known.

(a) I I   (b) I I   (c) I I   (d) I I   (e) I I

63. A cathode ray is:
(a) a beam of fast moving electrons.
(b) a dangerous ray emitted by a high power laser.
(c) due to secondary emission from the cathode.
(d) an E-M wave emitted when the primary electrons strike the plate.
(e) a low-energy X-ray.

(a) I I   (b) I I   (c) I I   (d) I I   (e) I I

64. Sound waves contain what form of energy?
(a) Kinetic.   (b) Chemical.
(c) Potential.   (d) Electrical.
(e) Heat.

(a) I I   (b) I I   (c) I I   (d) I I   (e) I I

65. One reason for using a series tuned circuit between the transmitter output and the transmission line to attenuate harmonics is that:
(a) it will offer a low impedance to the fundamental frequency and a high impedance to the harmonics.
(b) it will behave as a high pass filter and therefore will not let the harmonics pass.
(c) it will behave as a low pass filter and produce high attenuation of the harmonics.
(d) it will not attenuate the harmonics created by class C operation.
(e) Both (a) and (c) are true.

(a) I I   (b) I I   (c) I I   (d) I I   (e) I I

66. A lead-acid type storage battery is fully charged and has an amp-hour rating of 120 A-hr. Normally this battery can deliver 15 A of current for:
(a) 8 hr   (b) 15 hr
(c) 22.5 hr   (d) 12 hr
(e) There is not enough information to answer the question.

(a) I I   (b) I I   (c) I I   (d) I I   (e) I I

67. The emitter-collector resistance of an NPN transistor is being measured by an ohmmeter (using a 1.5 V battery), with the positive probe attached to the collector. If the collector and base leads are then connected together, the:
(a) ohmmeter reading will be unchanged.
(b) ohmmeter reading will increase.
(c) ohmmeter reading will decrease.
(d) ohmmeter will read a short circuit.
(e) None of the above is correct.

(a) I I   (b) I I   (c) I I   (d) I I   (e) I I

68. When low level modulation is used in an AM transmitter, the RF stages following the modulated stage cannot be:
(a) operated in class A.
(b) operated in class B.
(c) operated in class C.
(d) frequency multipliers.
(e) Both (c) and (d) are true.

(a)‖   (b)‖   (c)‖   (d)‖   (e)‖

69. A vertical 1/4 wave-length nondirectional antenna is properly tuned and radiating energy equally well through 360° in the horizontal plane. The space occupied by one-half cycle of the closest electrostatic field produced by the antenna is determined by:
(a) the atmospheric conditions.
(b) I^2 x R.
(c) the frequency.
(d) the type of antenna being used.
(e) the voltage at the ends of the antenna.

(a)‖   (b)‖   (c)‖   (d)‖   (e)‖

70. In high frequency transmitters, the use of hollow conductors is permissible because of:
(a) skin effect.
(b) their lower dielectric loss.
(c) proximity effect.
(d) Q factor.
(e) reduced weight.

(a)‖   (b)‖   (c)‖   (d)‖   (e)‖

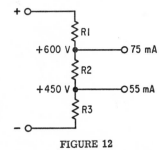

FIGURE 12

71. The circuit in Fig. 12 represents a voltage divider that is supplying voltages and load currents as shown. The bleeder current in the voltage divider is 5 mA. The value of R2 is:
(a) 10 kohms.   (b) 5.25 kohms.
(c) 7.5 kohms.   (d) 2.5 kohms.

(e) 3.4 kohms.

(a)‖   (b)‖   (c)‖   (d)‖   (e)‖

72. The result of using negative feedback in audio amplifiers is to:
(a) stabilize the voltage gain against changes in the parameters of the active device.
(b) improve the frequency response.
(c) reduce the amplitude and phase distortion.
(d) change the input and output impedances.
(e) All the above are true.

(a)‖   (b)‖   (c)‖   (d)‖   (e)‖

73. What stage is missing from the block diagram shown in Fig. 13, which represents an AM superheterodyne receiver used for telephony?
(a) The limiter.
(b) The beat frequency oscillator.
(c) The local oscillator.
(d) The discriminator.
(e) The carrier oscillator.

(a)‖   (b)‖   (c)‖   (d)‖   (e)‖

74. An advantage of a hollow pressurized cable over a solid dielectric cable is its:
(a) higher voltage breakdown rating for a given inner diameter.
(b) greater power handling capability for a given inner diameter.
(c) greater flexibility.
(d) easier installation.
(e) Both (a) and (b) are true.

(a)‖   (b)‖   (c)‖   (d)‖   (e)‖

75. The UHF spectrum covers the following frequency range:
(a) 3 to 30 MHz.   (b) 30 to 300 MHz.
(c) 300 MHz to 3 GHz. (d) 3 to 30 GHz.
(e) 30 to 300 GHz.

(a)‖   (b)‖   (c)‖   (d)‖   (e)‖

76. The antenna current reading of an FM transmitter is fluctuating. The reason may be:
(a) that the carrier is being modulated by the audio.
(b) a defective limiter in the modulator.
(c) an inadequate deviation ratio.
(d) grid bias variations in the final stage.
(e) a defective deviation limiter.

(a)‖   (b)‖   (c)‖   (d)‖   (e)‖

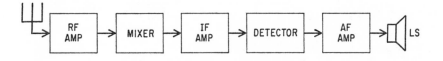

FIGURE 13

77. Reluctance is:
(a) the reciprocal of conductance.
(b) equal to $(L \times \mu)/A$.
(c) equal to magnetomotive force/flux.
(d) the reciprocal of inductance.
(e) the magnetic equivalent of current.

(a) I I   (b) I I   (c) I I   (d) I I   (e) I I

78. If one quarter of a cycle of an ac sine-wave occurs in 1 millisec, the frequency is:
(a) 4 Hz   (b) 1000 Hz   (c) 250 Hz
(d) 400 Hz   (e) 4 kHz

(a) I I   (b) I I   (c) I I   (d) I I   (e) I I

79. In connection with an ac, directly heated tube filament, the use of the center-tap connection of a filament transformer for the plate and grid signal returns:
(a) makes it possible to run heaters in parallel when the heater voltages are different.
(b) prolongs the life of the transformer.
(c) can prevent ac hum from appearing in the tube's output signal.
(d) is always used with indirectly heated filaments.
(e) None of the above are true.

(a) I I   (b) I I   (c) I I   (d) I I   (e) I I

80. What is the turns ratio required to match 3200 ohms on the primary side to an 8 ohm speaker?
(a) 400 to 1   (b) 1 to 40   (c) 1 to 20
(d) 20 to 1   (e) 1 to 4.5

(a) I I   (b) I I   (c) I I   (d) I I   (e) I I

81. For a receiving antenna to pick up a maximum signal, it must be:
(a) parallel with the magnetic field.
(b) perpendicular to the magnetic field.
(c) parallel with the electric field.
(d) perpendicular to the electric field.
(e) Both (b) and (c) are true.

(a) I I   (b) I I   (c) I I   (d) I I   (e) I I

82. One characteristic of a series wound dc motor is:
(a) high torque at low speeds.
(b) constant speed with changes of load.
(c) that a starting box is always required to control the speed of the motor.
(d) that the armature current is much greater than that of the field coil.
(e) that the motor races on full load.

(a) I I   (b) I I   (c) I I   (d) I I   (e) I I

83. Identify the circuit shown in Fig. 7 of Question 37. It is:
(a) a multivibrator.
(b) an RC phase shift oscillator.
(c) an audio amplifier with negative feedback.
(d) a phase splitter.

(e) Wien bridge oscillator.

(a) I I   (b) I I   (c) I I   (d) I I   (e) I I

84. The negative voltage probe of an ohmmeter is connected to the collector of a good PNP transistor while the positive probe is connected to the emitter. If a 470 kohm resistor is then connected between the collector and base, the ohmmeter:
(a) reading will be unchanged.
(b) reading will increase.
(c) reading will decrease.
(d) will indicate an open circuit.
(e) will indicate a short circuit.

(a) I I   (b) I I   (c) I I   (d) I I   (e) I I

85. Thermistor operation is similar to that of a:
(a) variable capacitor.
(b) variable resistor.
(c) variable inductor.
(d) reactance tube.   (e) varactor.

(a) I I   (b) I I   (c) I I   (d) I I   (e) I I

86. What would be the total impedance of a circuit with a resistance of 75 ohms in series with a parallel combination of an inductive reactance of 20 ohms, and a capacitive reactance of 25 ohms, across a supply voltage of 1,000 V?
(a) 125 ohms.   (b) 81.5 ohms.
(c) 75.2 ohms.   (d) 107.2 ohms.
(e) 87.4 ohms.

(a) I I   (b) I I   (c) I I   (d) I I   (e) I I

87. The power consumption of a station's transmitter is 425 W. It is operated for a total of 144 hr. How much electrical energy has been consumed?
(a) 0.425 kWh   (b) 61.2 kWh
(c) 7.23 kWh   (d) 42.5 kWh
(e) Less than 20 million joules.

(a) I I   (b) I I   (c) I I   (d) I I   (e) I I

88. A shunt is used with a VOM to:
(a) provide a zero adjustment control.
(b) increase the meter's voltage range.
(c) increase the meter's current range.
(d) increase the meter's resistance range.
(e) decrease the meter's resistance range.

(a) I I   (b) I I   (c) I I   (d) I I   (e) I I

89. A combination of stray inductance, stray capacitance and positive feedback in a transmitter can cause:
(a) subharmonic oscillations.
(b) harmonic radiation.
(c) parasitic oscillations.
(d) overheating of an RF amplifier.
(e) Both (c) and (d) are true.

(a) I I   (b) I I   (c) I I   (d) I I   (e) I I

90. A dummy antenna:
(a) is made from wood and used to test wind resistance.

(b) is a resistive load equal to the antenna radiation resistance.
(c) is a stand-by antenna.
(d) enables the transmitter to be tuned correctly without radiating a signal.
(e) Both (b) and (d) are true.

(a) I I   (b) I I   (c) I I   (d) I I   (e) I I

91. To generate frequencies in the SHF band, which of the following could be used?
(a) A grounded grid triode.
(b) A magnetron tube.
(c) A klystron tube.
(d) A traveling wave tube.
(e) (b), (c) and (d) are true.

(a) I I   (b) I I   (c) I I   (d) I I   (e) I I

92. If a class C amplifier is shunt-fed and the plate RF choke becomes an open-circuit, the:
(a) plate current will increase.
(b) plate current will be zero.
(c) plate current does not change.
(d) plate efficiency increases.
(e) RF output is badly distorted.

(a) I I   (b) I I   (c) I I   (d) I I   (e) I I

93. In a common-emitter stage, an emitter resistor is often included to:
(a) provide voltage regenerative feedback for reduced distortion of the signal.
(b) provide thermal stability for the stage.
(c) provide the base-biasing voltage.
(d) increase the gain of the stage.
(e) provide fixed-bias for the stage.

(a) I I   (b) I I   (c) I I   (d) I I   (e) I I

94. A 2 ohm cylindrical conductor is 2 ft long and has a diameter of 1/4 in. A second conductor, 8 ft long with a diameter of 1/2 in., is made from the same material. What is the resistance of the second conductor?
(a) 2 ohms.   (b) 0.5 ohm.   (c) 1 ohm.
(d) 0.25 ohm.   (e) 4 ohms.

(a) I I   (b) I I   (c) I I   (d) I I   (e) I I

95. In a series ac circuit, X_L is 2350 ohms, C is 0.005 μ F and R is 1850 ohms. What is the impedance at resonance?
(a) 4200 ohms.
(b) The frequency must be known.
(c) 500 ohms.   (d) 1.85 kohms.
(e) 2.1 kohms.

(a) I I   (b) I I   (c) I I   (d) I I   (e) I I

96. The plate of a pentode vacuum tube connected in a grounded cathode circuit will not be overheated by excessive:
(a) plate and screen supply voltage.
(b) filament voltage.
(c) plate current.
(d) grid bias.
(e) None of the above are true.

(a) I I   (b) I I   (c) I I   (d) I I   (e) I I

97. The cathode follower:
(a) is equivalent to a grounded emitter circuit.
(b) has its plate at ac ground and the input signal fed to the grid.
(c) is equivalent to a grounded base circuit.
(d) has an input impedance less than 1 kohm.
(e) has an output impedance greater than 1 Mohm.

(a) I I   (b) I I   (c) I I   (d) I I   (e) I I

98. The advantage of a delayed AVC circuit over a simple AVC circuit is its:
(a) greater reduction of the receiver's sensitivity on strong signals.
(b) greater reduction of the receiver's sensitivity on weak signals.
(c) large time delay on strong signals.
(d) short time delay on weak signals.
(e) characteristic of not developing AVC bias on weak signals.

(a) I I   (b) I I   (c) I I   (d) I I   (e) I I

99. When an absorption wavemeter is used to measure the frequency of a tank circuit, resonance is indicated by a:
(a) zero reading.
(b) sharp dip in the reading.
(c) maximum reading.
(d) minimum reading.
(e) zero beat.

(a) I I   (b) I I   (c) I I   (d) I I   (e) I I

100. The identifier or call letters of a Public Safety mobile station must be transmitted:
(a) at the beginning and end of each transmission or exchange.
(b) on the hour and half hour during operating hours.
(c) only when convenient between messages.
(d) Public Safety Service stations are government operated and do not have to transmit their call letters or identifiers.
(e) Both (a) and (b) are true.

(a) I I   (b) I I   (c) I I   (d) I I   (e) I I

Element 3, Test 5

1. When connecting a component or indicating device into a circuit, which of the following could be neglected with regards to polarity?
(a) Connecting a cathode resistor in a tube circuit.
(b) Connecting an RF thermocouple meter into an RF transmission line.
(c) Connecting a dc meter in a circuit.
(d) Connecting an electrolytic capacitor in a circuit.
(e) Both (a) and (b) are correct.
(a) I I   (b) I I   (c) I I   (d) I I   (e) I I

2. A Wheatstone bridge is used to measure:
(a) voltage.   (b) frequency.
(c) power.   (d) resistance.
(e) current.
(a) I I   (b) I I   (c) I I   (d) I I   (e) I I

3. In an ac series circuit, the capacitive reactance is double the inductive reactance. The inductive reactance is equal to the resistance. The phase angle between the source voltage and the current is:
(a) 0⁰   (b) 60⁰   (c) 180⁰   (d) 90⁰
(e) 45⁰
(a) I I   (b) I I   (c) I I   (d) I I   (e) I I

4. The frequency stability of an oscillator may be improved by:
(a) using a thermostatically controlled oven.
(b) using a high C-L ratio.
(c) using a buffer amplifier.
(d) stabilizing and regulating the power supplies.
(e) all the above are true.
(a) I I   (b) I I   (c) I I   (d) I I   (e) I I

5. An amplitude-modulated signal cannot be fed to a class C RF power amplifier because:
(a) the output modulation would be badly distorted.
(b) grid current flow would tend to clip the modulation peaks.
(c) the modulation envelope would be amplified linearly.

(d) the sidebands would not all receive the same amplification.
(e) (a), (b) and (c) are true.
(a) I I   (b) I I   (c) I I   (d) I I   (e) I I

6. Which of the drawings shown in Fig. 1 represents the vertical radiation pattern of a vertical Hertz antenna?
(a) I I   (b) I I   (c) I I   (d) I I   (e) I I

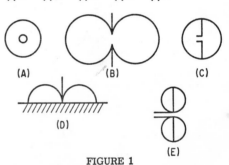

FIGURE 1

7. The maximum authorized bandwidth for Public Safety Radio Services type A3 emissions (part 89 of the FCC Rules and Regulations) shall be:
(a) 5 kHz   (b) 8 kHz   (c) 10 kHz
(d) 15 kHz   (e) 20 kHz
(a) I I   (b) I I   (c) I I   (d) I I   (e) I I

8. The potential on the base of a PNP transistor is +7.5 V with respect to ground. Which of the following is a possible potential on the emitter?
(a) +7.7 V   (b) -7.7 V   (c) +6.5 V
(d) -6.5 V   (e) 0 V
(a) I I   (b) I I   (c) I I   (d) I I   (e) I I

9. A three-phase, 60 Hz supply is rectified by a full-wave circuit. The ripple frequency is:
(a) 720 Hz   (b) 360 Hz   (c) 180 Hz
(d) 120 Hz   (e) 60 Hz
(a) I I   (b) I I   (c) I I   (d) I I   (e) I I

10. The time constant of an RC circuit is the time taken by the capacitor to acquire what percentage of its final voltage?
(a) 10%   (b) 50%   (c) 63.2%
(d) 70.7%   (e) 100%

(a)| | (b)| | (c)| | (d)| | (e)| |

11. Saturation of a ferromagnetic material is caused by:
(a) heating the material.
(b) striking the material.
(c) aligning most of the magnetic dipoles in a particular direction.
(d) preventing the formation of magnetic domains.
(e) placing the material in a high frequency magnetic field.

(a)| | (b)| | (c)| | (d)| | (e)| |

12. What is the essential change required for normal operation of the circuit shown in Fig. 2?
(a) Add a cathode by-pass capacitor.
(b) No changes are required.
(c) Add a capacitor to by-pass the B+.
(d) Include a plate load resistor.
(e) Both (a) and (d) are essential.

(a)| | (b)| | (c)| | (d)| | (e)| |

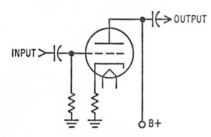

FIGURE 2

13. Assuming that the instantaneous frequency fed to a Foster-Seeley discriminator is equal to the IF, what is the phase relationship between the voltages developed across the primary and secondary windings of the input transformer?
(a) In phase.
(b) 45° out of phase.
(c) 90° out of phase.
(d) 135° out of phase.
(e) 180° out of phase.

(a)| | (b)| | (c)| | (d)| | (e)| |

14. A shunt-wound ac generator has 350 turns of wire on its armature and is producing 150 V at 15 A. Another ac shunt-wound generator is turning at the same speed and is similar in construction in all respects but has 700 turns of wire on its armature. How would the output frequency of the second generator compare to the output frequency produced by the first generator? It would:

(a) be doubled.
(b) be halved.
(c) be quadrupled.
(d) have a ratio of 4 to 1.
(e) The frequency would be the same.

(a)| | (b)| | (c)| | (d)| | (e)| |

15. In using the term "dynamic instability" with reference to an oscillator, we are not referring to the tendency of the oscillator to:
(a) shift frequency when a varying load is applied to the oscillator.
(b) be shifted in frequency during modulation.
(c) change in frequency when its plate and screen voltage is varied.
(d) shift in frequency when the grid voltage is varying.
(e) have uneven positive and negative amplitudes in the generated wave.

(a)| | (b)| | (c)| | (d)| | (e)| |

16. The schematic of Fig. 3 represents a part of an RCA double conversion communications receiver for operation in the 450 to 470 MHz band. The portion shown is the 14.5 MHz high IF stages of the receiver. The voltages shown are in reference to the supply's positive terminal (A+) that is not grounded to the chassis. If 15C29 is an open circuit, what will the result be?
(a) The IF output to the second mixer will increase.
(b) The collector current will increase.
(c) The collector current will decrease.
(d) The RF voltage at the collector will decrease.
(e) The emitter voltage will increase.

(a)| | (b)| | (c)| | (d)| | (e)| |

17. If 15C26 is an open circuit in the schematic of Fig. 3, what will be the result?
(a) An increased possibility of self-oscillation of the 15Q2 circuit will exist.
(b) The base voltage will decrease.
(c) The base voltage will increase.
(d) The stage is less stable with thermal changes.
(e) The emitter current will increase.

(a)| | (b)| | (c)| | (d)| | (e)| |

18. Thermal stability of 15Q2 in the schematic of Fig. 3 is found to be poor. Which of the following is a possible cause?
(a) 15C23 is an open circuit.
(b) There is a short circuit across 15R16.
(c) 15R13 is an open circuit.
(d) There is a short circuit across 15Q12.
(e) 15C27 is an open circuit.

(a)| | (b)| | (c)| | (d)| | (e)| |

19. A suitable input signal is present at the base of 15Q2 in the schematic of Fig. 3. When checking for signal voltage at the top of

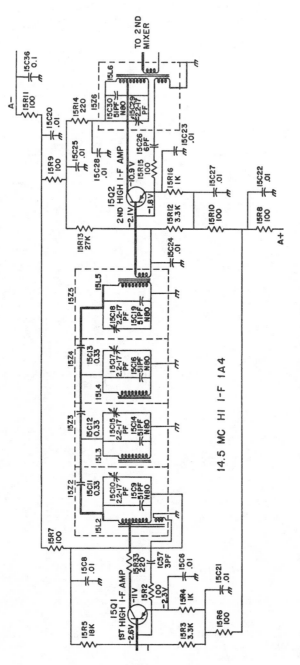

FIGURE 3 (Courtesy, RCA Corporation)

the 15L6 primary, the RF voltage is found to be zero. Which of the following is a true statement?
(a) 15Q2 is defective.
(b) 15R12 is an open circuit.
(c) This is a normal condition.
(d) 15R9 is an open circuit.
(e) There is a short circuit across 15R16.

(a) || (b) || (c) || (d) || (e) ||

20. The 15Q2 emitter voltage decreases to a very low negative value in the schematic of Fig. 3. Which of the following is a possible cause?
(a) The emitter of 15Q2 has opened internally.
(b) 15R13 is an open circuit.
(c) 15R12 is an open circuit.
(d) 15C23 is an open circuit.
(e) Both (a) and (b) are true.

(a) || (b) || (c) || (d) || (e) ||

21. Which of the following statements is not true about selenium diodes?
(a) They have a higher internal resistance than silicon diodes while conducting.
(b) They have a higher forward voltage drop than silicon diodes.
(c) They require heat sinks for high power applications.
(d) They are currently more commonly used than silicon diodes.
(e) They operate over a lower temperature range than silicon diodes.

(a) || (b) || (c) || (d) || (e) ||

22. A rectifier tube may use mercury vapor to:
(a) prolong the life of the tube.
(b) prevent electron bombardment of the cathode.
(c) prevent burn-out of the heater.
(d) reduce the internal voltage drop across the tube.
(e) reduce RF interference.

(a) || (b) || (c) || (d) || (e) ||

23. Two conductors with circular cross-sections are made of the same material and have the same length. If one conductor has a diameter four times as large as that of the other, the resistance of the larger wire will be:
(a) the same as that of the smaller conductor.
(b) sixteen times that of the smaller conductor.
(c) one-quarter that of the smaller conductor.
(d) four times that of the smaller conductor.
(e) one-sixteenth the resistance of the smaller conductor.

(a) || (b) || (c) || (d) || (e) ||

24. If the total power input to a communications system is 185 W, the electrical energy consumed in one day of continuous operation is:
(a) 3.48 kW   (b) 3.48 kWh
(c) 44.4 billion ergs (d) 4.44 kWh
(e) 34.8 kWh

(a) || (b) || (c) || (d) || (e) ||

25. The schematic shown in Fig. 4 is an RCA exciter, which is used in a mobile transmitter for operation in the 148 to 174 MHz range. The purpose of 23C20 is to:
(a) provide negative feedback from the collector circuit to the base circuit of 23Q5.
(b) provide signal coupling to 23Q5.
(c) decouple the collector circuit of 23Q5 from the power supply.
(d) resonate with the secondary winding of 23T1.
(e) None of the above are true.

(a) || (b) || (c) || (d) || (e) ||

26. In the schematic of Fig. 4, there is no RF output. Which of the following situations could cause this condition?
(a) 23L1 is open.
(b) 23C14 is open.
(c) The primary winding of 23T2 is open.
(d) 23C23 is open.
(e) Both (b) and (c) are true.

(a) || (b) || (c) || (d) || (e) ||

27. In the schematic of Fig. 4, the oscillator input signal and the audio input signal are normal, but there is an RF output signal that is not modulated. Which of the following is not a cause for this condition?
(a) 23R46 has a short across it.
(b) 23R46 is open.
(c) 23L1 is open.
(d) 23R13 is open.
(e) None of the above are true.

(a) || (b) || (c) || (d) || (e) ||

28. In the schematic of Fig. 4, the maximum frequency deviation of the transmitted RF signal is limited to ± 5 kHz by:
(a) 23CR2
(b) limiting the audio input signal amplitude.
(c) changing the oscillator input frequency.
(d) the value of L1.
(e) None of the above are true.

(a) || (b) || (c) || (d) || (e) ||

29. In the schematic of Fig. 4, with normal oscillator and audio inputs, there is no RF output. Which of the following is not a cause of this condition?
(a) 23C11 is shorted.
(b) 23C13 is open.
(c) 23C21 is shorted.
(d) 23C15 is open.

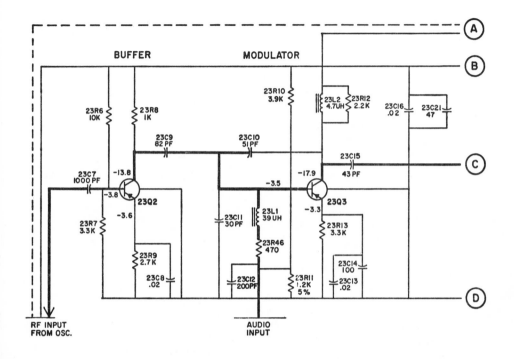

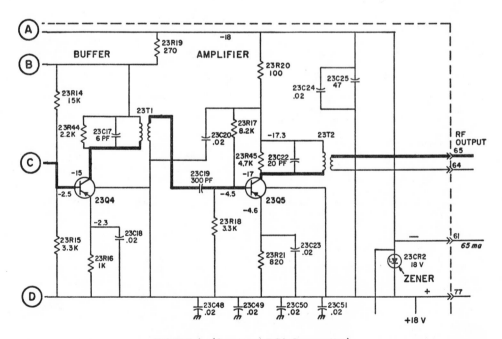

FIGURE 4   (Courtesy, RCA Corporation)

(e) 23R16 is open.

(a) I I   (b) I I   (c) I I   (d) I I   (e) I I

30. Which of the following is the most efficient type of rectifier?
(a) Silicon   (b) Selenium.
(c) Copper oxide.   (d) Hard diode.
(e) Mercury vapor.

(a) I I   (b) I I   (c) I I   (d) I I   (e) I I

31. Two resistors of 3.3 kohms and 4.7 kohms are connected in series across a 100 V source. Calculate the total power in the circuit.
(a) 1 W   (b) 1.25 W   (c) 8 W
(d) 110 W   (e) 12.5 W

(a) I I   (b) I I   (c) I I   (d) I I   (e) I I

32. The circuit shown in Fig. 5 represents a:
(a) M-derived T section filter.
(b) constant k high-pass filter.
(c) low-pass π filter.
(d) constant k low-pass filter.
(e) M-derived low-pass T filter.

(a) I I   (b) I I   (c) I I   (d) I I   (e) I I

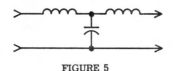

FIGURE 5

33. What must be added to the circuit of Fig. 6 for satisfactory operation?
(a) No additions are necessary.
(b) A screen resistor and by-pass capacitor must be added.
(c) A capacitor must be connected across the transformer primary to improve the frequency response.
(d) A decoupling network must be added to the plate circuit.

(e) A cathode resistor and a by-pass capacitor are necessary.

(a) I I   (b) I I   (c) I I   (d) I I   (e) I I

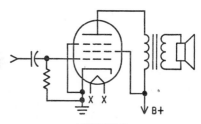

FIGURE 6

34. A transmitter has a carrier frequency of 680 kHz but the low pass filter following the final stage is defective. The radiated signal will not produce interference:
(a) with a transmitter operating on 2040 kHz.
(b) with a transmitter on 2720 kHz.
(c) on a near-by television receiver.
(d) with a transmitter on 340 kHz.
(e) with a transmitter on 1360 kHz.

(a) I I   (b) I I   (c) I I   (d) I I   (e) I I

35. The circuit shown in Fig. 7 is:
(a) a second detector.
(b) a local oscillator and a mixer.
(c) an IF amplifier.
(d) an RF amplifier and a first detector.
(e) a second detector and a pentagrid BFO.

(a) I I   (b) I I   (c) I I   (d) I I   (e) I I

36. If an AM transmitter with A3 emission is modulated by a sinusoidal 400 Hz tone, a 1.4 MHz carrier wave would contain frequencies of:
(a) 1.396 and 1.404 MHz.
(b) all frequencies from 1.3996 through 1.4004 MHz.
(c) 1.3996, 1.4 and 1.4004 MHz.
(d) 1.396, 1.4 and 1.404 MHz.

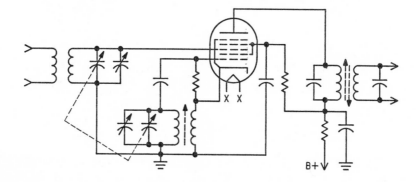

FIGURE 7

(e) None of the above are true.

(a) I I   (b) I I   (c) I I   (d) I I   (e) I I

37. Which of the following statements is true regarding SSSC transmission?
(a) The carrier and one set of sidebands are completely suppressed so that the output signal contains only the other set of sidebands.
(b) The carrier output is reduced so that only a pilot carrier remains, and this is radiated with both sets of sidebands.
(c) The carrier power is reduced so that only a one-half power carrier remains, and this is radiated with one set of sidebands.
(d) The carrier is completely suppressed with both sets of sidebands radiated.
(e) Full power carrier is radiated with one set of sidebands.

(a) I I   (b) I I   (c) I I   (d) I I   (e) I I

38. The input to the primary of a power transformer is 110 V, 60 Hz. There is 330 V between one end of the secondary and a center tap. What is the turns ratio (primary to full secondary)?
(a) 1 to 3   (b) 3 to 1   (c) 1 to 6
(d) 6 to 1   (e) 1 to 9

(a) I I   (b) I I   (c) I I   (d) I I   (e) I I

39. A resistor is color coded yellow, violet, black and silver. Which of the following values lie within the resistor's tolerance?
(a) 51 ohms.   (b) 480 ohms.
(c) 550 ohms.   (d) 42 ohms.
(e) 40 ohms.

(a) I I   (b) I I   (c) I I   (d) I I   (e) I I

40. The high Q of a coil is directly associated with:
(a) a high power factor.
(b) good selectivity.
(c) the use of a laminated soft iron core for high frequencies.
(d) a wide bandwidth.
(e) a high resistance for the coil, compared with its reactance.

(a) I I   (b) I I   (c) I I   (d) I I   (e) I I

41. A carbon microphone:
(a) requires a dc supply voltage.
(b) produces hiss when the signal output is low.
(c) has a frequency response of 75 to 5000 Hz.
(d) has a high sensitivity.
(e) All the above are true.

(a) I I   (b) I I   (c) I I   (d) I I   (e) I I

42. Static interference in a receiver can be reduced by using:
(a) noise limiters.
(b) AM transmission.

(c) FM transmission and reception.
(d) AVC.
(e) Both (a) and (c) are true.

(a) I I   (b) I I   (c) I I   (d) I I   (e) I I

43. The frequency range of a wavemeter may be extended by using:
(a) additional tuning capacitors.
(b) padding capacitors.
(c) trimming capacitors.
(d) additional crystals.
(e) plug-in coils.

(a) I I   (b) I I   (c) I I   (d) I I   (e) I I

44. An FM transmitter operating on a carrier frequency of 150 MHz is deviated 50%. What will be the carrier frequency when fully modulated?
(a) 149.9 MHz   (b) 150.0 MHz
(c) 151.1 MHz   (d) 151.2 MHz
(e) 200.0 MHz

(a) I I   (b) I I   (c) I I   (d) I I   (e) I I

45. For normal operation, the collector of a PNP transistor is:
(a) biased with a more positive voltage on the collector than the emitter.
(b) reverse-biased with respect to the base.
(c) forward-biased with respect to the base.
(d) maintained at the same potential as the emitter.
(e) maintained at the same potential as the base at all times.

(a) I I   (b) I I   (c) I I   (d) I I   (e) I I

46. The electrolyte used in a common dry cell contains:
(a) sal ammoniac.
(b) sulphuric acid.
(c) nickel hydroxide.
(d) potassium hydroxide.
(e) iron oxide.

(a) I I   (b) I I   (c) I I   (d) I I   (e) I I

47. In an ac circuit, the current lags the voltage by 35°. The power factor is:
(a) 35/360   (b) 0.35
(c) Sine 35°   (d) Cosine 35°
(e) Tangent 35°

(a) I I   (b) I I   (c) I I   (d) I I   (e) I I

48. The wattmeter:
(a) has two fixed current coils in series.
(b) has two fixed coils in parallel.
(c) can only measure apparent power.
(d) has a leading power factor.
(e) does not consider the phase relationship between the voltage and current.

(a) I I   (b) I I   (c) I I   (d) I I   (e) I I

49. An RF harmonic generator stage is required for:
(a) a reactance tube FM modulator.
(b) an overtone crystal oscillator.

(c) a frequency multiplier.
(d) an indirect phase modulator.
(e) a regenerative frequency divider.

(a) | | (b) | | (c) | | (d) | | (e) | |

50. The input resistance at the feedpoint of a resonant Marconi antenna is 35 ohms. The current at the feedpoint is 4 A RMS. What is the transmitter's operating power?
(a) 56 W   (b) 560 W   (c) 15 W
(d) 140 W   (e) 280 W

(a) | | (b) | | (c) | | (d) | | (e) | |

51. A telecommunications system for the transmission of fixed images that are recorded in a permanent form is:
(a) wire-photos.
(b) facsimile.
(c) slowed down television.
(d) designated as A3J emission.
(e) designated as P3D emission.

(a) | | (b) | | (c) | | (d) | | (e) | |

52. In a common-emitter amplifier, the emitter current is 5 mA and the base current is 100 μ A. The current gain is:
(a) 0.98   (b) 50   (c) 49   (d) 51
(e) 1.02

(a) | | (b) | | (c) | | (d) | | (e) | |

53. In a lead-acid storage cell, which of the following will not cause sulfation?
(a) Excessive internal temperature.
(b) Adding acid instead of properly charging.
(c) A low rate of trickle charge.
(d) Excessively high discharge rate.
(e) Prolonged periods of leaving the cell in a discharged condition.

(a) | | (b) | | (c) | | (d) | | (e) | |

54. A filter which is designed to attenuate severely all frequencies within a certain range but to pass through all frequencies above and below this range, is called a:
(a) high-pass filter.   (b) low-pass filter.
(c) band-pass filter.   (d) band-stop filter.
(e) resonant filter.

(a) | | (b) | | (c) | | (d) | | (e) | |

55. A gain of 10 dB is equivalent to a power ratio of:
(a) 10   (b) 20   (c) 100   (d) 1.0
(e) $\sqrt{10}$

(a) | | (b) | | (c) | | (d) | | (e) | |

56. The frequency response curve of an RC coupled audio amplifier:
(a) has a sine wave appearance.
(b) rises as the frequency is increased.
(c) falls as the frequency is increased.
(d) falls off at low frequencies and at high frequencies.

(e) may be improved by the use of regenerative feedback.

(a) | | (b) | | (c) | | (d) | | (e) | |

57. What is the approximate length of a quarter-wave Marconi antenna that is resonant at 300 MHz?
(a) 0.1 m   (b) 10 in.   (c) 0.5 m
(d) 10 m   (e) 0.025 m

(a) | | (b) | | (c) | | (d) | | (e) | |

58. A traveling wave tube (TWT) is generally used as:
(a) an SHF amplifier tube.
(b) a UHF oscillator tube.
(c) a modulator tube for an FM transmitter.
(d) a mixer tube for FM receivers.
(e) a converter tube for Loran signals.

(a) | | (b) | | (c) | | (d) | | (e) | |

59. In a phase inverter using a single transistor, the:
(a) output is taken from the collector and the emitter.
(b) gain of the stage is less than 1.0.
(c) circuit can be used to drive a push-pull amplifier.
(d) emitter and collector resistors are equal in value.
(e) All of the above are true.

(a) | | (b) | | (c) | | (d) | | (e) | |

60. A voltage doubler rectifier circuit charges each of its two capacitors from a 1:1 transformer operated from a 110 V, 60 Hz source. These capacitors are connected in series across the load, as shown in Fig. 8. The no-load dc output voltage is approximately:
(a) 155 V   (b) 220 V   (c) 311 V
(d) 440 V   (e) 465 V

(a) | | (b) | | (c) | | (d) | | (e) | |

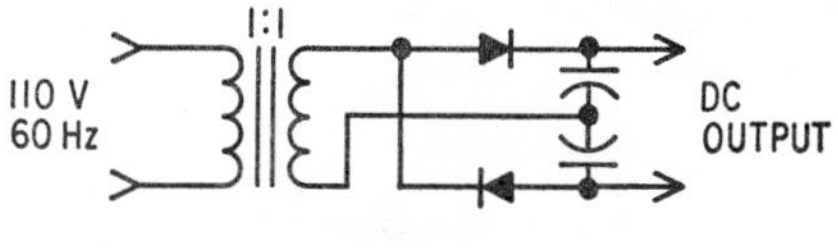

FIGURE 8

61. The magnetomotive force of a magnetic circuit is measured in:
(a) gauss.   (b) maxwells.   (c) henries.
(d) oersteds.   (e) gilberts.

(a) | | (b) | | (c) | | (d) | | (e) | |

62. A power transformer designed to operate on 110 V, 60 Hz is accidentally connected across a 110 V, 120 Hz source. The result would be that the:
(a) primary winding would burn out.
(b) turns ratio would double.
(c) copper losses would increase.

(d) primary current for a given load would increase.
(e) primary current for a given load would decrease.

(a) I I   (b) I I   (c) I I   (d) I I   (e) I I

63. If in an audio push-pull amplifier the plate current in each tube flows for approximately half the cycle of the input signal, the class of operation is:
(a) class A.   (b) class AB$_1$.
(c) class B   (d) class C.
(e) class AB$_2$.

(a) I I   (b) I I   (c) I I   (d) I I   (e) I I

64. The field strength of an electromagnetic wave is measured in:
(a) milliwatts per square meter.
(b) microvolts per meter.
(c) microamps per meter.
(d) lines per square centimeter.
(e) maxwells per square meter.

(a) I I   (b) I I   (c) I I   (d) I I   (e) I I

65. Within the klystron tube, the:
(a) external magnetic field causes the electrons to be focused into a narrow beam.
(b) electrons flowing through the cavity grids are alternately accelerated or retarded and are thereby caused to travel in bunches.
(c) electrons must be frequency modulated for proper operation of the tube.
(d) external magnetic field accelerates the electrons.
(e) repeller plate is made positive.

(a) I I   (b) I I   (c) I I   (d) I I   (e) I I

66. The heater element of a vacuum tube may be twisted to:
(a) increase cathode emission.
(b) increase the space charge.
(c) reduce hum.
(d) reduce cathode temperature.
(e) lower secondary emission effect.

(a) I I   (b) I I   (c) I I   (d) I I   (e) I I

67. The total resistance of 20, 5 and 4 ohm resistors connected in parallel is:
(a) 29 ohms.   (b) 8.33 ohms.
(c) 3.33 ohms.   (d) 2 ohms.
(e) 1.5 ohms.

(a) I I   (b) I I   (c) I I   (d) I I   (e) I I

68. A 27 ohm resistor is connected in series with an inductive reactance of 35 ohms. The total impedance is:
(a) 62 ohms.   (b) 9 ohms.
(c) 50.5 ohms.   (d) 44.2 ohms.
(e) 48.92 ohms.

(a) I I   (b) I I   (c) I I   (d) I I   (e) I I

69. The efficiency of a class A amplifier is approximately:

(a) less than 5%   (b) 25%   (c) 55%
(d) 78.5%   (e) 85%

(a) I I   (b) I I   (c) I I   (d) I I   (e) I I

70. An oscilloscope connected across the voice coil of the loudspeaker is being used in the alignment of an AM receiver. The output of the signal generator used must be:
(a) able to sweep continuously over the receiver's frequency range.
(b) unmodulated.
(c) a maximum at all times.
(d) modulated.
(e) maintained continuously at 455 kHz.

(a) I I   (b) I I   (c) I I   (d) I I   (e) I I

71. A high VSWR is caused by:
(a) a high-power input to a transmission line.
(b) the type of transmission line used.
(c) a mismatch between the transmission line's surge impedance and the load impedance.
(d) a low power input to a transmission line.
(e) a proper match between the source impedance and the load impedance.

(a) I I   (b) I I   (c) I I   (d) I I   (e) I I

72. The final RF stage in an FM transmitter employs fixed bias. A decrease in this bias would cause:
(a) over deviation.
(b) a lower percentage of modulation.
(c) an upward change in the antenna current.
(d) parasitic oscillations.
(e) a downward change of the antenna current when modulation is applied.

(a) I I   (b) I I   (c) I I   (d) I I   (e) I I

73. Which of the following types of bias requires the use of a grid leak resistor?
(a) Signal bias.   (b) Battery bias.
(c) Fixed bias.   (d) Bleeder bias.
(e) Cathode bias.

(a) I I   (b) I I   (c) I I   (d) I I   (e) I I

74. From tests, it is determined that an NPN transistor is not defective. An ohmmeter is connected between the emitter-collector junction with the negative voltage probe on the emitter and the positive voltage probe on the collector. If the emitter and base leads are then connected together, the:
(a) collector current will decrease.
(b) collector current will increase.
(c) collector current will fall to zero.
(d) ohmmeter reading will decrease.
(e) Both (b) and (d) are true.

(a) I I   (b) I I   (c) I I   (d) I I   (e) I I

75. In the circuit shown in Fig. 9, the source frequency is below the resonant frequency of L and C. If this frequency is now gradually

increased without changing the value of E, the output voltage would:
(a) fall at first and increase afterwards.
(b) rise at first and fall afterwards.
(c) fall continuously.
(d) rise continuously.
(e) remain constant.

(a) | | (b) | | (c) | | (d) | | (e) | |

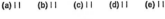
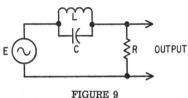

FIGURE 9

76. A quartz crystal has a fundamental frequency of 1275 kHz. What is the frequency of the fifth harmonic?
(a) 6.375 MHz   (b) 5,100 kHz
(c) 63,750 kHz   (d) 255 kHz
(e) 637.5 MHz

(a) | | (b) | | (c) | | (d) | | (e) | |

77. A grounded grid triode amplifier has an input impedance which is:
(a) higher than that of a cathode follower.
(b) greater than 1 Mohm.
(c) lower than that of a grounded cathode amplifier.
(d) higher than that of a class A push-pull amplifier.
(e) Both (a) and (d) are true.

(a) | | (b) | | (c) | | (d) | | (e) | |

78. At the output of a transmitter, the carrier power is measured as 300 W. The power in the second harmonic is 0.3 W. The second harmonic power is:
(a) 3 dB below the carrier power.
(b) 30 dB below the carrier power.
(c) 15 dB below the carrier power.
(d) 100 dB below the carrier power.
(e) 20 dB below the carrier power.

(a) | | (b) | | (c) | | (d) | | (e) | |

79. For a Public Safety Radio Services transmitter, the carrier frequency plate input to the final RF stage and the percent modulation must be checked:
(a) when the transmitter is first installed.
(b) at yearly intervals.
(c) when any change is made that will affect the parameters described in the question.
(d) when deemed necessary but not in excess of yearly intervals.
(e) All of the above are true.

(a) | | (b) | | (c) | | (d) | | (e) | |

80. With regard to the static plate dissipation of a vacuum tube, which of the following statements is false?
(a) It always exceeds the maximum power output in class A operation.
(b) It depends on the class of operation.
(c) It must not exceed the tube's rated plate dissipation.
(d) It is found from the product of the plate supply voltage and the signal component of the plate current.
(e) It can be found from the load line.

(a) | | (b) | | (c) | | (d) | | (e) | |

81. The schematic shown in Fig. 10 represents a crystal oscillator followed by a har-

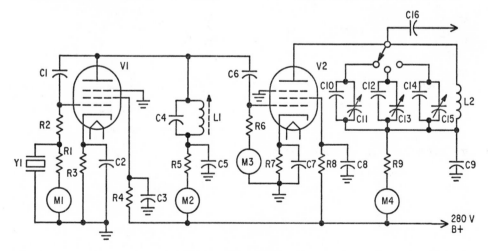

FIGURE 10

monic generator. The stages have been properly tuned and are operating correctly. M1, M2, M3 and M4 are dc current meters. If a short circuit appears across C3, which of the following results will occur?
(a) The reading of M1 will fall to zero.
(b) The reading of M2 will rise to a higher level.
(c) The reading of M3 will fall to zero.
(d) The reading of M4 will rise to a high value.
(e) All of the above are true.

(a) I I   (b) I I   (c) I I   (d) I I   (e) I I

82. In the schematic of Fig. 10, if the crystal is temporarily removed from its socket, which of the following results will occur?
(a) The reading of M1 will rise sharply.
(b) The reading of M2 will fall sharply.
(c) The reading of M3 will rise sharply.
(d) The reading of M4 will not change.
(e) None of the above will occur.

(a) I I   (b) I I   (c) I I   (d) I I   (e) I I

83. If temperature changes cause the value of C4 in the schematic of Fig. 10 to increase so that the combination of L1 and C4 is capacitive at the crystal resonant frequency, which of the following will occur?
(a) The reading of M1 will increase sharply.
(b) The reading of M2 will fall sharply.
(c) The reading of M3 will fall to zero.
(d) The reading of M4 will fall to zero.
(e) The output frequency increases.

(a) I I   (b) I I   (c) I I   (d) I I   (e) I I

84. The reading of M1 in the schematic of Fig. 10 falls to zero. Which of the following conditions is a possible cause?
(a) C3 is an open circuit.
(b) C4 is a short circuit.
(c) There is a short circuit across R2.
(d) There is a short circuit across R3.
(e) C5 is an open circuit.

(a) I I   (b) I I   (c) I I   (d) I I   (e) I I

85. In the schematic of Fig. 10, if C5 becomes a short circuit, which of the following results will occur?
(a) The reading of M1 will fall to zero.
(b) The reading of M2 will rise to a higher value.
(c) The reading of M3 will fall to zero.
(d) The reading of M4 will rise to a higher value.
(e) All the above are true.

(a) I I   (b) I I   (c) I I   (d) I I   (e) I I

86. In the schematic of Fig. 10, the reading of M4 rises. Which of the following conditions is a possible cause?
(a) The heater filament of V1 becomes an open circuit.
(b) C6 becomes a short circuit.

(c) C9 becomes an open circuit.
(d) R7 becomes an open circuit.
(e) Both (a) and (b) are true.

(a) I I   (b) I I   (c) I I   (d) I I   (e) I I

87. The reading of meter M3 in the schematic of Fig. 10 falls to zero. Which of the following conditions is a possible cause?
(a) An open circuit in the heater filament of V2.
(b) C7 is a short circuit.
(c) There is a short circuit across R4.
(d) There is a short circuit across R3.
(e) C2 is a short circuit.

(a) I I   (b) I I   (c) I I   (d) I I   (e) I I

88. The period of a radio frequency wave is found to be 0.0000001 sec. What is its wavelength?
(a) 3×10^8 m   (b) 3000 m
(c) 468 m   (d) 30 m
(e) 300 m

(a) I I   (b) I I   (c) I I   (d) I I   (e) I I

89. A milliammeter is set to the 100 mA scale and has an internal resistance of 0.5 ohm. To extend the current range, a shunt of 0.25 ohm is connected across the meter. When the meter reads 66 mA, the actual circuit current is:
(a) 22 mA   (b) 33 mA   (c) 66 mA
(d) 132 mA   (e) 198 mA

(a) I I   (b) I I   (c) I I   (d) I I   (e) I I

90. A low value carbon resistor has a few turns of copper wire wound around the resistor and connected across it. This combination is directly in series with the control grid. The purpose is to:
(a) frequency stabilize the oscillator.
(b) stabilize the output of an amplifier.
(c) provide additional bias.
(d) prevent parasitic oscillations.
(e) reduce the harmonic content of an amplifier output.

(a) I I   (b) I I   (c) I I   (d) I I   (e) I I

91. The velocity of propagation of radio waves:
(a) is three times greater in water than in air.
(b) increases in a medium where the dielectric constant is greater than 1.
(c) is approximately equal to 300,000,000 feet per second.
(d) decreases in a medium where the dielectric constant is greater than 1.
(e) is approximately equal to 186,000 meters per second.

(a) I I   (b) I I   (c) I I   (d) I I   (e) I I

92. A First-class or Second-class licensed operator is performing maintenance on a Public Safety Radio Services station trans-

mitter. Since he is a part time employee of the station, he:
(a) may not call another mobile station.
(b) cannot use the call sign of the station.
(c) must make entries in and sign the log.
(d) must not put the transmitter on the air.
(e) cannot repair damaged mobile base equipment.

(a) I I   (b) I I   (c) I I   (d) I I   (e) I I

93. The kink in a tetrode's plate current characteristic curve is caused by the:
(a) feedback due to interelectrode capacitance.
(b) emission saturation.
(c) low screen voltage.
(d) high cathode current.
(e) secondary emission from the plate.

(a) I I   (b) I I   (c) I I   (d) I I   (e) I I

94. A 500 ohm resistive load must carry a current of 0.2 A. Assuming that the only source available is 150 V dc, what value of resistance must be connected in series with the load?
(a) 25 ohms.   (b) 50 ohms.
(c) 250 ohms.   (d) 500 ohms.
(e) 2,500 ohms.

(a) I I   (b) I I   (c) I I   (d) I I   (e) I I

95. The time taken for 12 cycles of an ac sine wave is 3 sec. What is the frequency?
(a) 12 Hz   (b) 36 Hz   (c) 3 Hz
(d) 4 Hz   (e) 1/3 Hz

(a) I I   (b) I I   (c) I I   (d) I I   (e) I I

96. Square waves may be generated by:
(a) a multivibrator.
(b) an Armstrong oscillator.
(c) an RC phase shift oscillator.
(d) a reflex klystron.

(e) a neon tube using an RC circuit.

(a) I I   (b) I I   (c) I I   (d) I I   (e) I I

97. Compared with a class A amplifier, a class C stage using the same tube:
(a) creates less distortion in the plate current waveform.
(b) produces the same distortion.
(c) receives a lower peak-to-peak input signal.
(d) allows no grid current to flow.
(e) operates with a grid bias greater than the cut-off value of the tube.

(a) I I   (b) I I   (c) I I   (d) I I   (e) I I

98. The characteristic impedance of a transmission line is also known as the:
(a) surge impedance.
(b) source impedance.
(c) open circuit impedance.
(d) short circuit impedance.
(e) self impedance.

(a) I I   (b) I I   (c) I I   (d) I I   (e) I I

99. In a properly adjusted FM transmitter modulated by a single test tone, the average dc plate current fluctuates in:
(a) none of the transmitter stages.
(b) the master oscillator stage.
(c) all of the speech amplifiers.
(d) the radio frequency power amplifiers.
(e) the doubler and tripler stages.

(a) I I   (b) I I   (c) I I   (d) I I   (e) I I

100. The full load voltage of a power supply is 120 V and the percentage regulation is 10%. What is the no-load voltage output?
(a) 12 V   (b) 108 V   (c) 120 V
(d) 126 V   (e) 132 V

(a) I I   (b) I I   (c) I I   (d) I I   (e) I I

Element 3, Test 6

1. The deviation ratio of a frequency modulated transmitter is the ratio of the:
(a) maximum frequency swing to the maximum modulating frequency.
(b) operating frequency of the transmitter to the assigned frequency.
(c) frequency swing to the audio modulating frequency.
(d) maximum audio frequency to the minimum frequency swing.
(e) minimum audio frequency present to the maximum frequency swing.

(a) I I   (b) I I   (c) I I   (d) I I   (e) I I

2. In an FM transmitter, the amplitude of the audio signal is doubled, but its frequency is halved. The frequency deviation (disregarding pre-emphasis) is:
(a) doubled.   (b) halved.
(c) unchanged.   (d) multiplied by four.
(e) divided by four.

(a) I I   (b) I I   (c) I I   (d) I I   (e) I I

3. Which of the following test instruments is able to determine the resonant frequency of an LC circuit without applying power to the circuit under test?
(a) The grid dip meter.
(b) The heterodyne frequency meter.
(c) The absorption wave meter.
(d) The field strength meter.
(e) The reflectometer.

(a) I I   (b) I I   (c) I I   (d) I I   (e) I I

4. A "dip" is observed in an antenna current meter when AM is applied. The output RF stage is plate (amplitude) modulated. The "dip" would not be caused by:
(a) insufficient RF drive to the final stage.
(b) insufficient AF modulation.
(c) too low a level of grid bias of the modulated amplifier.
(d) poor regulation of a common power supply.
(e) an incorrect value of load impedance for the modulated amplifier.

(a) I I   (b) I I   (c) I I   (d) I I   (e) I I

5. To provide more than one output voltage from a power supply, the bleeder can be replaced by a:
(a) voltage doubler circuit.
(b) cascade multiplier.
(c) transformer with a step-down turns ratio.
(d) voltage divider.
(e) transformer with a step-up turns ratio.

(a) I I   (b) I I   (c) I I   (d) I I   (e) I I

6. The source readings in an ac circuit are as follows: voltage, 220 V at 60 Hz; current, 47 A; power factor, 0.73 lagging. What is the power consumption?
(a) 7.55 kW   (b) 9.37 kW
(c) 8.53 kW   (d) 10.34 kVA
(e) 6.37 kW

(a) I I   (b) I I   (c) I I   (d) I I   (e) I I

7. If in a dc circuit the voltage and the resistance have been measured, the power may be calculated from the formula:
(a) $P = I^2 R$ (b) $P = E/R$
(c) $P = E \times I$ (d) $P = E \times R$
(e) $P = E^2/R$

(a) I I   (b) I I   (c) I I   (d) I I   (e) I I

8. A class B AF power amplifier will produce low distortion only if:
(a) a parallel arrangement of two tubes is used.
(b) a push-push arrangement is used.
(c) a push-pull arrangement is used.
(d) control grid current is allowed to flow.
(e) the control grid excitation is kept to a low level with a single tube amplifier.

(a) I I   (b) I I   (c) I I   (d) I I   (e) I I

9. When modulating two transmitters with the same audio frequency, one with the A3 method and the other with the A3A method, the A3A transmission has:
(a) the same bandwidth as the A3 transmission.
(b) twice the bandwidth of the A3 transmission.

(c) one-half the bandwidth of the A3 transmission.

(d) the same RF power output as the A3 transmission during periods of no modulation.

(e) more total power in the sideband than the A3 transmitter when both are 100% modulated.

(a) I I   **(b)** I I   **(c)** I I   **(d)** I I   **(e)** I I

10. Which of the diagrams in Fig. 1 represents the RMS voltage and current distribution on a Hertz dipole?

(a) I I   **(b)** I I   **(c)** I I   **(d)** I I   **(e)** I I

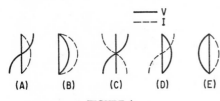

FIGURE 1

11. Class C amplifier bias is usually:
(a) at the projected cut-off point.
(b) at the cut-off point.
(c) at the mid-point of the transfer characteristic curve.
(d) two to four times the negative cut-off value.
(e) 0 V.

(a) I I   **(b)** I I   **(c)** I I   **(d)** I I   **(e)** I I

12. Voltage regulation in power supplies can be improved by using:
(a) a choke input filter rather than a capacitor input filter.
(b) a full wave rectifier rather than a half-wave circuit.
(c) a three-phase rather than a single-phase arrangement.
(d) a gaseous regulator tube circuit.

(e) All of the above are true.

(a) I I   **(b)** I I   **(c)** I I   **(d)** I I   **(e)** I I

13. The frequency at which a filter begins to provide attenuation to undesired frequencies is called the:
(a) cut-off frequency.
(b) band-stop frequency.
(c) decay frequency.
(d) resonant frequency.
(e) None of the above.

(a) I I   **(b)** I I   **(c)** I I   **(d)** I I   **(e)** I I

14. The best conductors contain atoms that:
(a) are pentavalent.
(b) contain many neutrons.
(c) have more electrons than protons.
(d) have a valence of one.
(e) have a valence of seven.

(a) I I   **(b)** I I   **(c)** I I   **(d)** I I   **(e)** I I

15. An amplifier delivers a power output of 20 W for an input signal power of 0.02 W. The amplifier gain is:
(a) + 20 dB   (b) - 20 dB
(c) + 100 dB   (d) - 100 dB
(e) + 30 dB

(a) I I   **(b)** I I   **(c)** I I   **(d)** I I   **(e)** I I

16. In the schematic shown in Fig. 2, how would the output of the final RF amplifier be affected if R1 were opened?
(a) The output of the amplifier would not be affected.
(b) The dc plate current would increase to a very high value and the reading of meter M1 would decrease.
(c) The amplifier's output would increase.
(d) The amplifier would self-oscillate and cause interference to other stations.
(e) The output of the amplifier would be much lower.

(a) I I   **(b)** I I   **(c)** I I   **(d)** I I   **(e)** I I

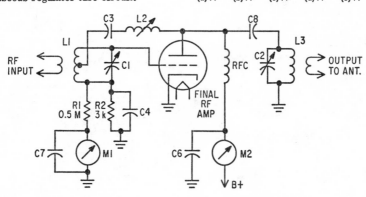

FIGURE 2

17. With reference to Fig. 2 of question 16, what parts could be eliminated without affecting circuit operation?
(a) This circuit will not work with L2 and C3 in the circuit and they should therefore be removed.
(b) R1, C7, M1, and M2 could be eliminated.
(c) R2 and C4 could be removed from the circuit.
(d) No changes could be made to reduce the number of parts in this circuit.
(e) C3 could be placed across C1, and L2 could be removed from the circuit.

(a) | | (b) | | (c) | | (d) | | (e) | |

18. Assuming that the amplifier in Fig. 2 of question 16 is a working circuit, which of the following types of modulation could not be used for it to amplify.
(a) Single sideband suppressed carrier operation.
(b) Frequency modulation.
(c) Amplitude modulation.
(d) Vestigial sideband TV.
(e) (a), (c) and (d).

(a) | | (b) | | (c) | | (d) | | (e) | |

19. A synchronous motor's speed depends primarily on the:
(a) number of pole pairs.
(b) line frequency applied to the motor.
(c) amount of current in the field.
(d) amount of current in the armature.
(e) Both (a) and (b) above are true.

(a) | | (b) | | (c) | | (d) | | (e) | |

20. The tank circuit load of an RF push-pull power amplifier may be tuned to:
(a) any odd harmonic of the input signal frequency.
(b) any even harmonic of the input signal frequency.
(c) any harmonic, either odd or even, of the input signal frequency.
(d) the fundamental frequency or any harmonic of the input signal frequency.
(e) only the fundamental frequency.

(a) | | (b) | | (c) | | (d) | | (e) | |

21. The main disadvantage of using a capacitor input filter with a full wave rectifier is:
(a) the low dc voltage output.
(b) the poor smoothing.
(c) the physical size of components required.
(d) poorer regulation compared with that of the choke input filter.
(e) its inability to be used with receivers.

(a) | | (b) | ᒪ   (c) | | (d) | | (e) | |

22. Impedance matching is used in RF amplifiers for:
(a) minimum distortion.
(b) improvement in frequency response.
(c) maximum power transfer.

(d) achieving the correct phase relationships.
(e) harmonic suppression.

(a) | | (b) | | (c) | | (d) | | (e) | |

23. What energy is consumed if a 100 W light bulb burns for 100 hr?
(a) 100 W   (b) 1000 W
(c) 10,000 W   (d) 100 kW
(e) None of the above.

(a) | | (b) | | (c) | | (d) | | (e) | |

24. The circuit shown in Fig. 3 represents a:
(a) push-pull amplifier.
(b) two stage audio amplifier with negative feedback.
(c) parallel tube amplifier.
(d) multivibrator.
(e) Colpitts oscillator.

(a) | | (b) | | (c) | | (d) | | (e) | |

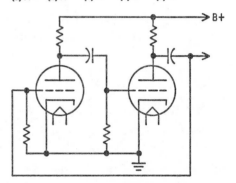

FIGURE 3

25. The maximum collector-to-emitter voltage rating indicates the maximum:
(a) collector supply voltage.
(b) voltage that can be safely applied between the collector and the emitter.
(c) forward voltage that can be applied to the collector-emitter junction.
(d) forward voltage that can be applied between the collector and the base with the emitter grounded.
(e) None of the above are true.

(a) | | (b) | | (c) | | (d) | | (e) | |

26. What changes (if any) are required for the correct operation of the class "B" push-pull audio amplifier shown in Fig. 4?
(a) C5 and R8 should be removed.
(b) R3 must be by-passed to ground.
(c) The screen grids of V4 and V5 should be connected directly to B+ instead of to the T2 primary.
(d) R7 must be by-passed.
(e) No changes are required, since this is a working circuit.

(a) | | (b) | | (c) | | (d) | | (e) | |

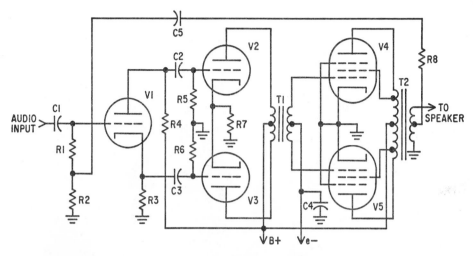

FIGURE 4

27. Klystrons are generally operated in the frequency range of:
(a) 600 MHz to 3 GHz
(b) 3 to 30 GHz
(c) 600 MHz to 30 GHz
(d) 6,000 MHz to 60 GHz
(e) 300 MHz to 6 GHz

(a) I I   (b) I I   (c) I I   (d) I I   (e) I I

28. Which of the following can produce a blackout of sky-wave communications?
(a) The troposphere.
(b) The earth's magnetic field.
(c) The peak of the sun spot cycle.
(d) Solar flares.
(e) Both (c) and (d) are true.

(a) I I   (b) I I   (c) I I   (d) I I   (e) I I

29. How would a receiver be adjusted to receive a signal on a lower frequency?
(a) Increase the capacitance of the tuning capacitor.
(b) Decrease the capacitance of the tuning capacitor.
(c) Decrease the inductance of the tuning coil.
(d) Reduce the coupling between the antenna and the tuned circuit.
(e) Sharpen the selectivity of the tuned circuit.

(a) I I   (b) I I   (c) I I   (d) I I   (e) I I

30. The stage gain of an amplifier is defined as:
(a) the grid signal voltage input to the following stage divided by the grid signal voltage input to the amplifier.
(b) the signal output voltage from the plate divided by the signal input voltage to the grid.

(c) being equal to the μ of the tube.
(d) being equal to $(\mu \times r_p)/(r_p + R_L)$.
(e) Both (a) and (b) are correct.

(a) I I   (b) I I   (c) I I   (d) I I   (e) I I

31. With excessive feedback in a crystal oscillator:
(a) the grid bias will decrease towards zero.
(b) the crystal may be overheated.
(c) the crystal may fracture.
(d) it is impossible to frequency modulate the oscillator in the normal way.
(e) Both (b) and (c) above are true.

(a) I I   (b) I I   (c) I I   (d) I I   (e) I I

32. The current range of a VOM can be extended using:
(a) a shunt.
(b) two VOMs in series.
(c) a multiplier resistor.
(d) an external capacitor.
(e) an impedance bridge.

(a) I I   (b) I I   (c) I I   (d) I I   (e) I I

33. Which of the following statements is not true?
(a) The RMS value is the value that will give the same heating effect as the same numerical value of dc.
(b) In an ac circuit, true power is the product of the voltage and the current and the power factor.
(c) The peak-to-peak value is twice the peak value.
(d) The RMS value equals the peak value divided by 1.414.
(e) The average value over the half cycle equals the peak-to-peak value multiplied by 0.6366.

(a) I I   (b) I I   (c) I I   (d) I I   (e) I I

34. An RF choke can be used to:
(a) offer high reactance to all frequencies.
(b) offer high reactance to RF currents but low reactance to AF currents.
(c) offer infinite impedance to dc.
(d) offer high reactance to AF currents but low reactance to RF currents.
(e) Both (a) and (c) above are true.

(a) | | (b) | | (c) | | (d) | | (e) | |

35. For maximum power transfer to the load in the circuit shown in Fig. 5, what must be the value of R?
(a) 4.3 ohms.   (b) 8.6 ohms.
(c) 0.43 ohm.   (d) 43 ohms.
(e) 2.15 ohms.

(a) | | (b) | | (c) | | (d) | | (e) | |

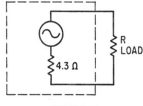

FIGURE 5

36. A common-base transistor amplifier has:
(a) high current gain.
(b) in-phase input and output signals.
(c) very low voltage gain.
(d) a high input impedance.
(e) a low output impedance.

(a) | | (b) | | (c) | | (d) | | (e) | |

37. A5C emission signifies:
(a) amplitude modulation, television, vestigial sideband transmission.
(b) amplitude modulation, telephony, with two sets of sidebands.
(c) amplitude modulation, multichannel voice-frequency telephone, single sideband, reduced carrier.
(d) amplitude modulation, single sideband, suppressed carrier.
(e) amplitude modulation, facsimile, with modulation of the main carrier either directly or by a frequency modulated subcarrier.

(a) | | (b) | | (c) | | (d) | | (e) | |

38. Sparking at the brushes of a dc motor or generator is not normally caused by:
(a) open field coils.
(b) dirt on the commutator.
(c) brushes not in the neutral position.
(d) weak brush tension.
(e) overloading the motor.

(a) | | (b) | | (c) | | (d) | | (e) | |

39. A quarter wavelength antenna that is 0.5 m long is to be mounted on an automobile.

The best position would be on the:
(a) roof.
(b) front bumper on the driver's side.
(c) front bumper away from the driver's side.
(d) rear bumper on the driver's side.
(e) rear bumper away from the driver's side.

(a) | | (b) | | (c) | | (d) | | (e) | |

40. The functional diagram shown in Fig. 6 is an RCA (four channel model) mobile communications unit for use in the 406 to 470 MHz range. The unit is constructed with replaceable modules as follows: TU1-4A transmitter oscillator; TU2 transmitter mike amplifier; TU3 transmitter modulator; TU4 transmitter RF driver; TU5 transmitter RF power amplifier; RU1 receiver preselector (RF amp, first mixer); RU2 first receiver IF amplifier; RU3 first receiver IF filter; RU4 second receiver mixer; RU5 second receiver IF filter; RU6 second receiver IF amplifier; RU7 receiver discriminator; RU8 receiver audio frequency amplifier; RU9 receiver squelch; RU10 receiver oscillator. There is no RF output on channel 1. All other channels are normal. Which of the following conditions is a possible cause?
(a) TU1-4A oscillator is defective.
(b) TU3 modulator is defective.
(c) TU4 driver is defective.
(d) Switch 3 is defective.
(e) Both (a) and (d) are true.

(a) | | (b) | | (c) | | (d) | | (e) | |

41. If in the functional diagram of Fig. 6 there is no noise or audio output, the most likely fault is to be found in which of the following module groups?
(a) RU1, RU2 and RU3.
(b) RU3, RU4 and RU10.
(c) RU4, RU5 and RU6.
(d) RU7, RU8 and RU9.
(e) All the above are true.

(a) | | (b) | | (c) | | (d) | | (e) | |

42. If in the functional diagram of Fig. 6 the receiver exhibits faulty squelch operation but performs normally otherwise, the most likely fault is to be found in which of the following module groups?
(a) RU1, RU2 and RU3.
(b) RU1, RU9 and RU10.
(c) RU7 and RU9.
(d) RU5, RU6 and RU7
(e) RU5, RU6 and RU9.

(a) | | (b) | | (c) | | (d) | | (e) | |

43. In the functional diagram of Fig. 6, the receiver has poor sensitivity. It receives only strong signals with excessive noise on desired signals. Which of the following

statements would be the least likely to be true?
(a) The antenna connection is faulty.
(b) The preselector RU1 module is faulty.
(c) The first IF RU2 module is faulty.
(d) The second mixer RU4 module is faulty.
(e) The oscillator RU10 module is faulty.

(a) I I   (b) I I   (c) I I   (d) I I   (e) I I

44. In the functional diagram of Fig. 6 there is no transmitter RF output. When the driver module TU4 is replaced, then there is a reduced RF output. What is a possible cause for this effect?
(a) The replacement driver module is not properly tuned.
(b) The power amplifier module is detuned by the new driver module.
(c) The modulator module is detuned by the new driver module.
(d) The oscillator module is detuned by the new driver module.
(e) Both (c) and (d) are true.

(a) I I   (b) I I   (c) I I   (d) I I   (e) I I

45. If in the functional diagram of Fig. 6 the proper RF output is present but with lower than normal modulation, what module might be at fault?
(a) The TU2 mike amplifier.
(b) The TU3 modulator.
(c) The TU4 driver.
(d) The TU5 power amplifier.
(e) Both (a) and (b) are true.

(a) I I   (b) I I   (c) I I   (d) I I   (e) I I

46. When a semiconductor PN junction is forward biased:
(a) only minority charge carriers can cross the junction.
(b) a negative voltage is applied to the P-type material and a positive voltage is applied to the N-type material.
(c) it presents a high resistance to the flow of current through it.
(d) it presents a low resistance to the flow of current through it.
(e) the depletion region is wider than when the junction is reverse-biased.

(a) I I   (b) I I   (c) I I   (d) I I   (e) I I

47. F1 emission signifies:
(a) frequency (or phase) modulation, telegraphy by frequency shift keying without the use of a modulating audio frequency--one of two frequencies being emitted at any instant.
(b) frequency (or phase) modulation, telephony.
(c) frequency (or phase) modulation, television.
(d) facsimile by direct frequency modulation of the carrier.

(e) cases that are not covered by any other classification using frequency modulation.

(a) I I   (b) I I   (c) I I   (d) I I   (e) I I

48. A 1/4 wavelength vertical antenna radiates equally well:
(a) in all directions.
(b) in all vertical directions.
(c) in all horizontal directions.
(d) bidirectionally.
(e) unidirectionally.

(a) I I   (b) I I   (c) I I   (d) I I   (e) I I

49. A device has a voltage gain of 1000, and the input and output resistances are designed to be the same. The gain is:
(a) 20 dB   (b) 30 dB   (c) 40 dB
(d) 60 dB   (e) 100 dB

(a) I I   (b) I I   (c) I I   (d) I I   (e) I I

50. What governs the dc (or quiescent) level of plate current in a pentode?
(a) The plate load resistor.
(b) The cathode bias resistor.
(c) The dc voltage on the screen grid.
(d) The value of B+ supply voltage for the plate and the screen grid.
(e) All of the above are true.

(a) I I   (b) I I   (c) I I   (d) I I   (e) I I

51. In a parallel resonant LC circuit, the Q is:
(a) $(1/R) \times \sqrt{C/L}$
(b) equal to the resonant frequency divided by the bandwidth.
(c) equal to the resistance divided by the inductive reactance.
(d) a measure of the power magnification.
(e) measured in cycles.

(a) I I   (b) I I   (c) I I   (d) I I   (e) I I

52. A full wave rectifier circuit has a pulsating dc output with a 200 V peak. What working voltage rating should the filter capacitors have to insure a reasonable safety factor.
(a) 100 V   (b) 127 V   (c) 141.4 V
(d) 200 V   (e) 250 V

(a) I I   (b) I I   (c) I I   (d) I I   (e) I I

53. An FM transmitter oscillator operates on a frequency of 29.0 MHz, and the transmitter uses three doublers to generate its output. The transmitter's unmodulated output frequency is:
(a) 232 MHz   (b) 4.8333 MHz
(c) 3.2650 MHz   (d) 783.00 MHz
(e) None of the above are true.

(a) I I   (b) I I   (c) I I   (d) I I   (e) I I

54. A lead-acid storage battery has an internal resistance of 2 ohms and is connected to a 12 V, 4 W lamp. How much current will flow through the lamp?
(a) 0.333 A   (b) 0.111 A

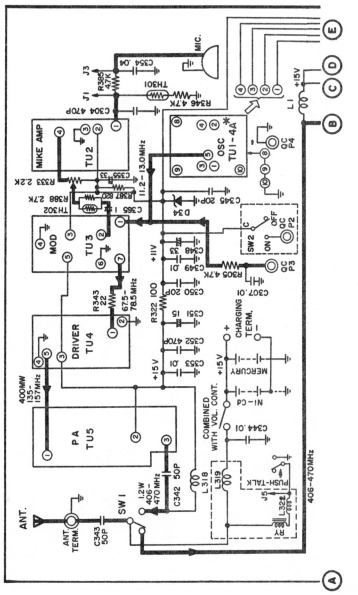

FIGURE 6

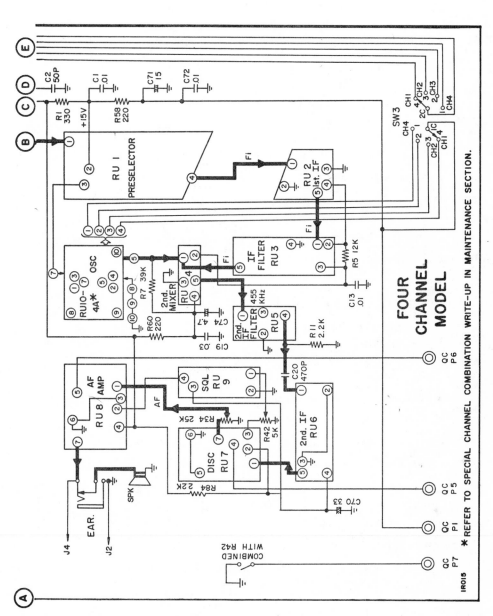

FIGURE 6   (Courtesy, RCA Corporation)

(c) 0.316 A   (d) 0.600 A
(e) 2.4 A

(a) | | (b) | | (c) | | (d) | | (e) | |

55. An operator removes the supply voltage
from the plate circuit of an RF power amplifier stage. The plate tuning capacitor is
then rocked through resonance while he ob-
serves the grid current meter. The operator is checking for:
(a) resonance in the plate circuit.
(b) drive from the previous stage.
(c) parasitic oscillations.
(d) the correct frequency output.
(e) neutralization.

(a) | | (b) | | (c) | | (d) | | (e) | |

56. The secondary RMS voltage feeding a
half-wave rectifier with a capacitor input filter is 150 V. The dc output voltage under
light loads will be approximately:
(a) 150 V   (b) 212 V   (c) 300 V
(d) 442 V   (e) 600 V

(a) | | (b) | | (c) | | (d) | | (e) | |

57. Transformers with air cores are:
(a) used at audio frequencies.
(b) designed with inductances on the order
     of henries.
(c) used at radio frequencies.
(d) used to reduce size and weight problems
     of portable audio amplifiers.
(e) more efficient than iron core transform-
     ers at a frequency of 1 kHz.

(a) | | (b) | | (c) | | (d) | | (e) | |

58. The output of a push-push stage contains:
(a) the fundamental and all odd harmonics of
     the input signal frequency.
(b) the fundamental and all even harmonics
     of the input signal frequency.
(c) the fundamental and all harmonics of the
     input signal frequency.
(d) only even harmonics of the input signal
     frequency.
(e) only odd harmonics of the input signal
     frequency.

(a) | | (b) | | (c) | | (d) | | (e) | |

59. Positive feedback between several vacuum tube audio amplifier stages using a common B+ supply can be eliminated by:
(a) including RC decoupling networks in the
     plate circuits.
(b) raising the values of the plate load re-
     sistors.
(c) increasing the cathode bias.
(d) increasing the values of the coupling ca-
     pacitors.
(e) increasing the values of the grid resis-
     tors.

(a) | | (b) | | (c) | | (d) | | (e) | |

60. Regarding the schematic shown in Fig. 7,
which of the following is a false statement?
(a) The circuit is a common collector stage.
(b) The circuit is an emitter follower stage.
(c) The circuit has a high input impedance
     and a low output impedance.
(d) The circuit has a low current gain but a
     high voltage gain.
(e) The output signal is in phase with the in-
     put signal.

(a) | | (b) | | (c) | | (d) | | (e) | |

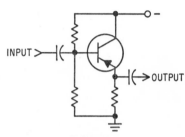

FIGURE 7

61. When measuring the collector to ground
voltage in the schematic shown in Fig. 8, the
base is accidentally shorted to ground.
Which of the following results would occur?
(a) The transistor would be severely damag-
     ed.
(b) The collector current will not change
     appreciably.
(c) The collector voltage will be less posi-
     tive.
(d) The collector voltage will be more posi-
     tive.
(e) The collector voltage will go slightly
     negative.

(a) | | (b) | | (c) | | (d) | | (e) | |

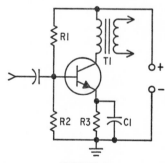

FIGURE 8

62. In the schematic of Fig. 8, the forward
bias on the transistor is found to be low, but
the collector current reads high. Which of
the following is a possible cause?
(a) The transistor has a collector-emitter
     short.
(b) R1 is an open circuit.

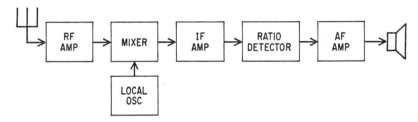

FIGURE 9

(c) R3 is an open circuit.
(d) C1 is an open circuit.
(e) There is a short circuit across the primary of T1.

(a) | | (b) | | (c) | | (d) | | (e) | |

63. Propagation in a waveguide is produced by means of:
(a) electromagnetic waves.
(b) transverse electrostatic waves only.
(c) transverse magnetic waves only.
(d) longitudinal electrostatic waves.
(e) an electron stream.

(a) | | (b) | | (c) | | (d) | | (e) | |

64. Receiver interference will not be reduced by using:
(a) a plastic enclosure around the receiver.
(b) a noise limiter.
(c) a crystal filter.
(d) a wave-trap.
(e) an RF amplifier.

(a) | | (b) | | (c) | | (d) | | (e) | |

65. The block diagram shown in Fig. 9 is:
(a) an SSSC receiver.
(b) a double conversion AM superheterodyne receiver.
(c) a single conversion AM superheterodyne receiver.
(d) a single conversion FM superheterodyne receiver.

(e) a double conversion FM superheterodyne receiver.

(a) | | (b) | | (c) | | (d) | | (e) | |

66. The circuit shown in Fig. 10 is a pentode audio voltage amplifier. Which of the following statements is true?
(a) The circuit is using contact bias.
(b) The circuit is using cathode bias.
(c) The circuit should not use the type of bias shown.
(d) The circuit is using a fixed bias.
(e) The bias is zero.

(a) | | (b) | | (c) | | (d) | | (e) | |

67. Most ac meters are calibrated to read:
(a) peak value
(b) average value.
(c) peak to peak value.
(d) root mean square value.
(e) instantaneous value.

(a) | | (b) | | (c) | | (d) | | (e) | |

68. A 110 V, 60 Hz source is connected across an ideal capacitor. In this circuit the:
(a) capacitor has no effect on the current.
(b) voltage and the current are 180° out of phase.
(c) voltage lags the current by 90°.
(d) current lags the voltage by 90°.
(e) current lags the voltage by 45°.

(a) | | (b) | | (c) | | (d) | | (e) | |

69. Which of the following will not help in eliminating parasitic oscillations?
(a) Redesigning the layout of the amplifier.
(b) Shortening leads in the plate and grid circuits.
(c) Placing a small resistor-inductor parallel combination in series with the grid.
(d) Placing a small resistor-inductor parallel combination in series with the plate.
(e) Biasing the grid to a linear section of the transfer characteristic curve.

(a) | | (b) | | (c) | | (d) | | (e) | |

70. Each resistor shown in Fig. 11 has a resistance of 10 ohms. Which combination will have a total resistance of 15 ohms?

(a) | | (b) | | (c) | | (d) | | (e) | |

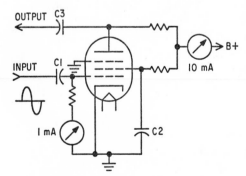

FIGURE 10

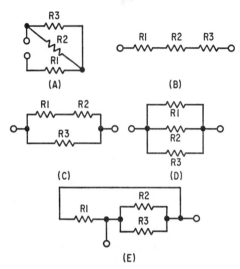

(A)   (B)

(C)   (D)

(E)

FIGURE 11

71. To determine the dc plate input power of the final stage of a transmitter:
(a) a wattmeter must be used.
(b) multiply the plate voltage by the plate resistance.
(c) divide the plate voltage by the plate current.
(d) multiply the plate supply voltage by the plate current.
(e) multiply the square of the plate voltage by the plate current.

(a) I I   (b) I I   (c) I I   (d) I I   (e) I I

72. Which of the following is an advantage of grid modulation in producing AM?
(a) Less distortion in the modulation envelope.
(b) Greater linearity.
(c) Modulation percentage is easier to adjust.
(d) The sideband power is supplied by the modulator.

(e) Less audio power required.
(a) I I   (b) I I   (c) I I   (d) I I   (e) I I

73. In Fig. 12, if C2 should become shorted:
(a) M1 would read higher.
(b) M1 would read zero, and M2 would read higher.
(c) M2 would read lower.
(d) M2 would read lower, and M1 would read higher.
(e) None of the above are true, for both meters would read normally.

(a) I I   (b) I I   (c) I I   (d) I I   (e) I I

74. In Fig. 12, if meter M1 becomes open, then:
(a) M1 would oscillate.
(b) M2 would read lower.
(c) M1 would read zero.
(d) M2 would read higher.
(e) Both (b) and (c) are correct.

(a) I I   (b) I I   (c) I I   (d) I I   (e) I I

75. The authorized bandwidth (after Nov. 1, 1967) for FM stations in the Public Safety Radio Services operating within the frequency range of 450 through 470 MHz is:
(a) 10 kHz   (b) 20 kHz   (c) 25 kHz
(d) 40 kHz   (e) 5 kHz

(a) I I   (b) I I   (c) I I   (d) I I   (e) I I

76. An antenna is to receive radio waves equally well from any direction in the horizontal plane. The transmitted waves are vertically polarized. A suitable type would be a:
(a) horizontal antenna using a parasitic array.
(b) horizontal omnidirectional antenna.
(c) horizontal loop antenna.
(d) horizontal unidirectional antenna.
(e) vertical omnidirectional antenna.

(a) I I   (b) I I   (c) I I   (d) I I   (e) I I

77. An IF transformer has been replaced in a receiver, but no signal generator is available to align the IF stages accurately. A rough alignment can be carried out by:

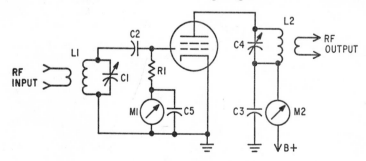

FIGURE 12

(a) selecting a strong signal and adjusting the IF transformer for minimum AVC voltage.
(b) tuning off a station and peaking up the IF transformer for maximum noise output.
(c) selecting a weak station and peaking the IF transformer for maximum signal output.
(d) rendering the local oscillator inoperative and peaking the IF transformer while tuned to a strong station for maximum AVC voltage.
(e) setting the ferrite slugs of the IF transformer to their mid-positions.

(a) I I   (b) I I   (c) I I   (d) I I   (e) I I

78. Overmodulation is undesirable in an AM system because it:
(a) creates unwanted sidebands.
(b) creates distortion in the audio signal.
(c) increases the current drain on the plate supply of the output stage.
(d) introduces pre-emphasis into the audio output of the receiver's detector.
(e) Both (a) and (b) are true.

(a) I I   (b) I I   (c) I I   (d) I I   (e) I I

79. The frequency stability of a crystal oscillator may be improved by:
(a) increasing the feedback to the crystal.
(b) increasing the value of the B+ voltage.
(c) increasing tension on the crystal.
(d) using a separate regulated power supply for the crystal oscillator stage.
(e) Both (a) and (b) are true.

(a) I I   (b) I I   (c) I I   (d) I I   (e) I I

80. An inductor with an adjustable ferrite core is resonant with a fixed capacitor. If the core was partially out of the coil and is then inserted deeper into the coil, the result will be to:
(a) decrease the inductance.
(b) decrease the resonant frequency.
(c) increase the resonant frequency.
(d) leave the resonant frequency unchanged.
(e) Both (a) and (c) are true.

(a) I I   (b) I I   (c) I I   (d) I I   (e) I I

81. What is the reactance of a 0.003 μ F capacitor at a frequency of 500 kHz?
(a) 106 ohms   (b) 1.06 mhos
(c) 10.6 ohms   (d) 1.06 ohms
(e) 1060 ohms

(a) I I   (b) I I   (c) I I   (d) I I   (e) I I

82. If the cathode by-pass capacitor is removed from an audio amplifier stage, the:
(a) bias would fall to zero and grid current would flow.
(b) amplitude distortion would increase.
(c) plate dissipation would increase.

(d) gain would decrease but there would be an improvement in the frequency response.
(e) gain would increase but the frequency response would be reduced.

(a) I I   (b) I I   (c) I I   (d) I I   (e) I I

83. For Public Safety Radio Services stations of 3 W or more, crystal-controlled oscillators must have their carrier frequency checked at least:
(a) bimonthly.   (b) once a day.
(c) once a week.   (d) once a month.
(e) once a year.

(a) I I   (b) I I   (c) I I   (d) I I   (e) I I

84. The final amplifier of a transmitter uses a push-pull RF amplifier and is fixed biased, with the filament of each tube being supplied by a separate transformer. If the filament of one tube were to burn out, the result would be:
(a) a change in the output frequency of the carrier.
(b) a reduced signal output with severe distortion.
(c) a complete loss of the carrier output.
(d) a reduction of the second order harmonic content.
(e) a reduced output, with an increase in even harmonic content.

(a) I I   (b) I I   (c) I I   (d) I I   (e) I I

85. A vacuum tube oscillator is producing an output if:
(a) there is a reading on the grid current meter.
(b) an RF voltage exists at the plate.
(c) while tuning the plate tank circuit, the plate current meter indicates a dip.
(d) there is a negative bias on the grid.
(e) All the above are true.

(a) I I   (b) I I   (c) I I   (d) I I   (e) I I

86. The ac plate resistance of a triode is the:
(a) ratio of a small change in plate voltage to a small change in grid voltage.
(b) ratio of a small change in plate voltage to a small change in plate current.
(c) ratio of a small change in plate current to a small change in grid voltage.
(d) ratio of a small change in grid voltage to a small change in plate current.
(e) ratio of a small change in plate voltage to a small change in grid current.

(a) I I   (b) I I   (c) I I   (d) I I   (e) I I

87. A 0.2 mH inductor with a resistance of 150 ohms is connected in parallel with a 0.0033 μ F capacitor. What is the resonant frequency of the tank circuit?
(a) 6220 kHz   (b) 195.7 kHz

(c) 622 kHz   (d) 62 MHz
(e) 19. 7 MHz

(a) I I   (b) I I   (c) I I   (d) I I   (e) I I

88. The luminous haze that sometimes occurs at the surface of conductors carrying high voltages is called:
(a) corona discharge.
(b) photoemission.
(c) the ionosphere.
(d) space charge.
(e) luminance.

(a) I I   (b) I I   (c) I I   (d) I I   (e) I I

89. Public Safety Radio Services stations may be operated without a station authorization for a period of:
(a) not more than one week.
(b) not more than three months.
(c) not more than one month.
(d) not more than 48 hr.
(e) None of the above are true.

(a) I I   (b) I I   (c) I I   (d) I I   (e) I I

90. Which of the following is not a factor in determining the surge impedance of a line?
(a) The radius of the conductors.
(b) The dielectric constant of the insulating material.
(c) The spacing between the conductors.
(d) The length of the conductors.
(e) The ratio of the distributed inductance to the distributed capacitance.

(a) I I   (b) I I   (c) I I   (d) I I   (e) I I

91. What is the phase angle between the control grid voltage and the cathode current in a triode AF amplifier with a resistive plate load?
(a) 0° (b) 45° (c) 90° (d) 180°
(e) 270°

(a) I I   (b) I I   (c) I I   (d) I I   (e) I I

92. The ratio of a small change in plate voltage to a corresponding small change in grid voltage that will restore the plate current to its original value is called the:
(a) ac plate resistance.
(b) transconductance.
(c) conversion conductance.
(d) amplification factor.
(e) amplifier gain.

(a) I I   (b) I I   (c) I I   (d) I I   (e) I I

93. In an ac circuit containing reactance, the product of the source voltage and the source current is called:
(a) average power.   (b) reactive power.
(c) idle power.   (d) true power.
(e) apparent power.

(a) I I   (b) I I   (c) I I   (d) I I   (e) I I

94. If the frequency of the source feeding a bridge rectifier is 60 Hz, the fundamental

ripple frequency contained in the output will be:
(a) 30 Hz   (b) 60 Hz   (c) 90 Hz
(d) 120 Hz   (e) 180 Hz

(a) I I   (b) I I   (c) I I   (d) I I   (e) I I

95. The maximum ratings on data sheets for transistors:
(a) are not applicable if heat sinks are used.
(b) may all be exceeded if heat sinks are used.
(c) apply only at 65^oC ambient temperature.
(d) define absolute maximum and minimum values, none of which should be exceeded.
(e) may all be exceeded if short duty cycle pulses are used.

(a) I I   (b) I I   (c) I I   (d) I I   (e) I I

96. It is not necessary to submit a formal application for modification of a Public Safety Radio Services station license if your plan is to:
(a) change the carrier frequency.
(b) increase the output power.
(c) add an auxiliary control on-off switch.
(d) increase the antenna height.
(e) None of the above are true.

(a) I I   (b) I I   (c) I I   (d) I I   (e) I I

97. If a quarter wavelength section of transmission line whose surge impedance is Z_0 is terminated by a load Z, the input impedance Z_{in} is:
(a) $\sqrt{Z \times Z_0}$ (b) $(Z + Z_0)/2$
(c) $(Z - Z_0)/2$ (d) Z_0^2/Z
(e) Z^2/Z_0

(a) I I   (b) I I   (c) I I   (d) I I   (e) I I

98. In a class A audio amplifier, the input signal and the bias are such that the plate current is flowing continuously. For what fraction of the cycle does the control grid current flow?
(a) It does not flow at all.
(b) For less than a quarter of a cycle.
(c) For one-half of a cycle.
(d) For between one-half and three-quarters of a cycle.
(e) It will flow throughout the cycle.

(a) I I   (b) I I   (c) I I   (d) I I   (e) I I

99. The maximum dc cathode current rating of a tube refers to the maximum:
(a) continuous dc current that the cathode can supply without serious deterioration of the oxide coating of the cathode.
(b) current that can be allowed to flow from the cathode to the plate.
(c) current that can be allowed to flow from the cathode to grid number 1 and the plate.
(d) peak surge current that can be allowed to flow from the cathode to all other electrodes.

(e) current that can be allowed to flow from the cathode to the control grid, the beam forming plates and the plate.

(a) I I   (b) I I   (c) I I   (d) I I   (e) I I

100. The circuit shown in Fig. 13 uses:
(a) capacitive coupling.
(b) inductive coupling.
(c) tuned primary--tuned secondary coupling.
(d) mutual inductive coupling.

(e) link coupling.

(a) I I   (b) I I   (c) I I   (d) I I   (e) I I

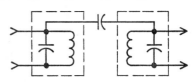

FIGURE 13

Element 3, Test 7

1. Neutralization in a vacuum-tube amplifier is:
(a) never used in modern communications equipment.
(b) essential for pentode RF amplifiers.
(c) used to cancel feedback through the control grid-plate capacitance.
(d) important in AF triode power amplifiers.
(e) never necessary in a push-pull circuit.

(a) I I (b) I I (c) I I (d) I I (e) I I

2. A 1 MHz RF carrier is amplitude modulated by a 1 kHz audio note. The total sideband spectrum extends from:
(a) 1000 to 1001 kHz (b) 999 to 1000 kHz
(c) 1000 to 1002 kHz (d) 998 to 1000 kHz
(e) 999 to 1001 kHz

(a) I I (b) I I (c) I I (d) I I (e) I I

3. A police radio service transmitter is subject to what frequency tolerance?
(a) 0.00001% (b) 0.0005%
(c) 0.005% (d) 0.002%
(e) It is subject to the type of station license, power, and frequency used.

(a) I I (b) I I (c) I I (d) I I (e) I I

4. Prior FCC approval must be obtained:
(a) for repairing any part of a transmitter.
(b) for changes that result in operation inconsistent with the terms of the Commission's instrument of authority.
(c) for substitution of like FCC approved units.
(d) before changing a crystal for a new one operating on the same frequency.
(e) before replacing the power output tube with one of the same type number.

(a) I I (b) I I (c) I I (d) I I (e) I I

5. When using a heterodyne-frequency meter, zero beat occurs if:
(a) two frequencies are identical.
(b) one frequency is an exact harmonic of the other.
(c) the calibration check point frequency and the transmitter's AF modulation frequency are identical.
(d) the AF modulation frequency of the frequency meter and the transmitter's carrier frequency are identical.
(e) Both (a) and (b) are true.

(a) I I (b) I I (c) I I (d) I I (e) I I

6. An advantage of an FSK transmission over a CW signal is that:
(a) the noise produces less interference.
(b) the transmitter power output is constant.
(c) the receiver AVC bias is constant.
(d) in the transmitter, keying occurs only at the oscillator stage.
(e) All of the above are true.

(a) I I (b) I I (c) I I (d) I I (e) I I

7. The maximum external control grid to cathode resistance means the:
(a) value of grid leak resistor that will allow the space charge to cut off the plate current in the tube.
(b) maximum resistance that can be used to provide self bias.
(c) highest value of external resistance that should be connected between the grid and cathode.
(d) highest value of resistance that can be connected in series between the control grid and the coupling capacitor for stabilization purposes.
(e) highest value of V_g/I_g permitted for that type of tube.

(a) I I (b) I I (c) I I (d) I I (e) I I

8. An HF crystal operating near an odd multiple of its fundamental frequency is known as:
(a) a shear mode crystal.
(b) a flexural mode crystal.
(c) an AT crystal.
(d) an overtone crystal.
(e) a crystal multiplier.

(a) I I (b) I I (c) I I (d) I I (e) I I

9. A half wave rectifier circuit uses a 110 V, 60 Hz source and a transformer with a 1 to 3 step-up ratio. What is the approximate value of the dc output voltage with no load?
(a) 165 V (b) 330 V (c) 234 V

(d) 467 V   (e) 990 V

(a) || (b) || (c) || (d) || (e) ||

10. Hysteresis loss in power transformers occurs in:
(a) the core.
(b) the primary winding.
(c) the secondary winding.
(d) both primary and secondary windings.
(e) insulation between the windings.

(a) || (b) || (c) || (d) || (e) ||

11. The time constant in seconds of a resistor-capacitor circuit is found by:
(a) multiplying the resistance in ohms by the capacitive reactance.
(b) dividing the resistance in ohms by the capacitance in farads.
(c) taking the reciprocal of (b) above.
(d) multiplying the resistance in ohms by the capacitance in farads.
(e) dividing the capacitive reactance by the resistance in ohms.

(a) || (b) || (c) || (d) || (e) ||

12. Beta cut-off frequency of a transistor amplifier is:
(a) the frequency at which the current gain becomes zero.
(b) the frequency at which the current gain of a common base transistor stage has decreased to 0.707 of its low frequency value.
(c) always higher than alpha cut-off value.
(d) the frequency at which the gain is 3 dB lower than at 1000 Hz.
(e) the same as the alpha cut-off value.

(a) || (b) || (c) || (d) || (e) ||

13. Motor and generator brushes often have capacitors placed between the brushes and ground. Why?
(a) To produce greater torque or higher power output.
(b) To increase the armature voltage output.
(c) To reduce RF interference.
(d) To reduce the sparking that occurs at the field.
(e) Both (c) and (d) are true.

(a) || (b) || (c) || (d) || (e) ||

14. An antenna has an electrical length of 120°. In terms of wavelength, the antenna is:
(a) less than a quarter wavelength long.
(b) longer than a quarter wavelength but shorter than a half wavelength.
(c) longer than a half wavelength but shorter than three quarters of a wavelength.
(d) longer than three quarters of a wavelength but shorter than a wavelength.
(e) longer than a wavelength.

(a) || (b) || (c) || (d) || (e) ||

15. In the circuit shown in Fig. 1, what is the value of the transistor's beta?
(a) 29   (b) 37   (c) 49   (d) 50   (e) 51

(a) || (b) || (c) || (d) || (e) ||

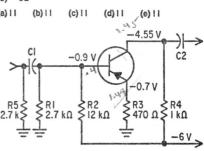

FIGURE 1

16. In the circuit of Fig. 1, the base to ground potential is measured and found to be zero. Which of the following is a possible cause?
(a) R2 is an open circuit.
(b) There is a short across R3.
(c) R4 is an open circuit.
(d) There is a short across R2.
(e) Both (a) and (b) are true.

(a) || (b) || (c) || (d) || (e) ||

17. In the circuit of Fig. 1, if R3 is defective and is an open circuit, which of the following statements is false?
(a) The emitter to ground potential is measured and found to be zero.
(b) The base to ground potential is measured and found to be -0.9 V.
(c) The collector to ground potential is measured and found to be -6 V.
(d) The emitter, base and collector currents are all zero.
(e) The current through R2 is approximately 0.41 mA.

(a) || (b) || (c) || (d) || (e) ||

18. In the circuit of Fig. 1, the collector to ground potential is measured and found to be approximately -0.9 V. Which of the following is a possible cause?
(a) R4 is an open circuit.
(b) There is a short across R4.
(c) R3 is an open circuit.
(d) There is a short across R3.
(e) The collector has opened internally.

(a) || (b) || (c) || (d) || (e) ||

19. In the circuit of Fig. 1, the emitter has opened internally. Which of the following statements is true?
(a) The collector to ground potential will be zero.
(b) The emitter terminal to ground potential will be zero.

(c) The base to ground potential will be zero.
(d) The base to ground potential will be -0.9 V.
(e) Both (b) and (d) are true.

(a) | | (b) | | (c) | | (d) | | (e) | |

20. In the circuit of Fig. 1, the collector to ground potential is measured and found to be -6 V. Which of the following is a possible cause?
(a) R4 is an open circuit.
(b) There is a short across R3.
(c) R1 is an open circuit.
(d) R2 is an open circuit.
(e) Nothing is wrong since the potential measured is within the range of normal operation.

(a) | | (b) | | (c) | | (d) | | (e) | |

21. When driving a conventional vacuum-tube audio amplifier, the carbon microphone:
(a) requires a transformer for impedance matching.
(b) has a high inherent noise level (hiss).
(c) has a limited frequency response.
(d) has high sensitivity.
(e) All the above are true.

(a) | | (b) | | (c) | | (d) | | (e) | |

22. The ratio of a small change in plate current to a small change in grid voltage when the plate voltage is kept constant is called the:
(a) transconductance.
(b) conversion conductance.
(c) mutual conductance.
(d) ac plate conductance.
(e) Both (a) and (c) are true.

(a) | | (b) | | (c) | | (d) | | (e) | |

23. A series ac circuit contains a resistance of 5 ohms, a capacitive reactance of 20 ohms and an inductive reactance of 8 ohms. What is the voltage across the inductor if the source voltage is 39 V?
(a) 13 V   (b) 24 V   (c) 36 V
(d) 16 V   (e) 8 V

(a) | | (b) | | (c) | | (d) | | (e) | |

24. Decreasing the Q of a tank circuit:
(a) increases the resonant frequency.
(b) raises its impedance.
(c) decreases its bandwidth.
(d) increases the current magnification.
(e) None of the above are true.

(a) | | (b) | | (c) | | (d) | | (e) | |

25. The major advantage of the tetrode junction transistor over the conventional junction transistor is:
(a) a higher operating temperature range.
(b) greater stability over the operating temperature range.
(c) its higher operating frequency.

(d) a higher noise factor.
(e) the simpler biasing arrangements used.

(a) | | (b) | | (c) | | (d) | | (e) | |

26. Type "AO" emission is:
(a) amplitude modulation telephony, double sideband.
(b) carrier for amplitude modulation, but without modulation.
(c) amplitude modulation, vestigial sideband, television.
(d) amplitude modulation, suppressed carrier.
(e) amplitude modulation, multichannel voice-frequency, single sideband, reduced carrier.

(a) | | (b) | | (c) | | (d) | | (e) | |

27. Overheating in a motor-generator set is not caused by which of the following?
(a) Dirt in the bearings.
(b) Improper lubrication.
(c) Bearings not properly aligned on the shaft.
(d) Excess load on the motor or generator.
(e) A reactive load.

(a) | | (b) | | (c) | | (d) | | (e) | |

28. The field strength of a transmitter is measured as 50 μ V per meter. This means that:
(a) the voltage induced in a Hertz dipole located 1 m from the transmitter antenna is 50 μ V.
(b) at a particular location, the voltage induced in a conductor 1 m long and placed at right angles to the electric field is 50 μ V.
(c) the voltage induced in a Marconi antenna decreases 50 μ V for every meter the antenna is moved further away from the transmitter.
(d) the voltage induced in a conductor 1 m long and placed parallel with the electric field is 50 μ V.
(e) the voltage induced in a conductor 1 m long and placed 1 km from the antenna is 50 μ V.

(a) | | (b) | | (c) | | (d) | | (e) | |

29. At UHF, the greatest loss in a coaxial cable with air as the dielectric is the:
(a) radiation loss.
(b) dielectric loss.
(c) copper loss.
(d) eddy current loss.
(e) hysteresis loss.

(a) | | (b) | | (c) | | (d) | | (e) | |

30. With regard to an electron coupled oscillator, which of the following is a false statement?
(a) This type of oscillator does not require a buffer stage.

(b) This oscillator has good frequency stability.

(c) Frequency multiplication is possible at the oscillator output.

(d) Coupling between the grid and plate circuits is achieved by means of the electron stream through the tube.

(e) The oscillator must be crystal-controlled.

(a) I I   (b) I I   (c) I I   (d) I I   (e) I I

31. A triode RF power amplifier employing grid-leak bias has the following operating conditions: B+ = 1000 V, I_b = 100 mA, I_g = 10 mA, grid leak resistor = 4.7 kohms, heater current = 2 A. What is the value of the grid bias?
(a) 4.7 V   (b) 47 V   (c) 470 V
(d) 9.4 V   (e) 100 V

(a) I I   (b) I I   (c) I I   (d) I I   (e) I I

32. As measured at a 110 V, 60 Hz source, the current is 0.75 A and a wattmeter records 50 W. The power factor is:
(a) 0.606   (b) 0.293   (c) 0.575
(d) 0.182   (e) 0.736

(a) I I   (b) I I   (c) I I   (d) I I   (e) I I

33. A 4 ohm speaker may be connected to the plate circuit of an audio amplifier by means of:
(a) capacitive coupling.
(b) a transformer with a step up ratio.
(c) an output transformer with a step down ratio.
(d) direct coupling.
(e) RC coupling.

(a) I I   (b) I I   (c) I I   (d) I I   (e) I I

34. If excessive direct current flows through a filter choke, the choke's inductance may:
(a) be unchanged.
(b) rise sharply.
(c) decrease due to core saturation.
(d) resonate with the filter capacitor at the ripple frequency.
(e) act as a capacitance.

(a) I I   (b) I I   (c) I I   (d) I I   (e) I I

35. What type of modulation is mainly associated with static interference?
(a) amplitude modulation.
(b) frequency modulation.
(c) phase modulation.
(d) angle modulation.

(e) PFM.

(a) I I   (b) I I   (c) I I   (d) I I   (e) I I

36. A3H emission indicates an amplitude modulation:
(a) for telephony, single sideband, full carrier.
(b) for telephony, single sideband, reduced carrier.
(c) for telephony, single sideband, suppressed carrier.
(d) facsimile (with modulation of the main carrier either directly or by an amplitude modulated subcarrier).
(e) multichannel voice frequency telephony, single sideband, reduced carrier.

(a) I I   (b) I I   (c) I I   (d) I I   (e) I I

37. Grid-dip meters are not used for:
(a) generating a signal.
(b) adjusting wavetraps.
(c) checking the frequency determining network of an oscillator.
(d) measuring the resonant frequency of a transmitter's tank circuit.
(e) measuring RF currents.

(a) I I   (b) I I   (c) I I   (d) I I   (e) I I

38. In the transmitter block diagram shown in Fig. 2, the oscillator stage alone is on frequency. Which would be the next stage to be tuned?
(a) 2   (b) 3   (c) 4   (d) 5   (e) 6

(a) I I   (b) I I   (c) I I   (d) I I   (e) I I

39. The plate tank circuit of a push-push circuit may be tuned to select:
(a) either the fundamental frequency or an odd harmonic of the input signal frequency.
(b) either the fundamental frequency or an even harmonic of the input signal frequency.
(c) any odd harmonic but not the fundamental frequency.
(d) any even harmonic but not the fundamental frequency.
(e) the fundamental frequency only.

(a) I I   (b) I I   (c) I I   (d) I I   (e) I I

40. The highest fundamental frequency to which a crystal can normally be cut is approximately:
(a) 500 kHz   (b) 1 MHz   (c) 5 MHz
(d) 10 MHz   (e) 25 MHz

(a) I I   (b) I I   (c) I I   (d) I I   (e) I I

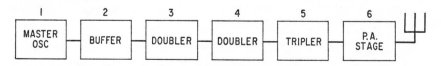

FIGURE 2

41. An IF pentode has the following operating conditions: plate supply voltage, +250 V; screen grid voltage, +160 V; plate current, 10 mA; screen current, 2 mA. What value of screen dropping resistor is required?
(a) 125 kohms.   (b) 80 kohms.
(c) 45 kohms.   (d) 25 kohms.
(e) 16 kohms.

(a) I I   (b) I I   (c) I I   (d) I I   (e) I I

42. Which of the following expressions represents the true power in a series LCR circuit?
(a) $E \times I$ (b) I^2R
(c) $I^2 \times Z$ (d) E^2/Z
(e) $I^2 \times X_L$

(a) I I   (b) I I   (c) I I   (d) I I   (e) I I

43. A resistor is color coded red, red, red. What is its tolerance?
(a) 20%   (b) 2%   (c) 10%   (d) 1%
(e) Not enough information is given for a solution.

(a) I I   (b) I I   (c) I I   (d) I I   (e) I I

44. A problem that may exist with long horizontal waveguides is:
(a) an increase in the waveguide's impedance, causing matching difficulties.
(b) a reduction in velocity that will increase the waveguide losses.
(c) moisture accumulation.
(d) a decrease in the waveguide's impedance, causing matching difficulties.
(e) the difficulty in producing a high voltage standing wave ratio.

(a) I I   (b) I I   (c) I I   (d) I I   (e) I I

45. When a class C RF amplifier is plate modulated, its average dc plate current does not change. This indicates:
(a) a normal condition.
(b) insufficient grid excitation.
(c) excessive grid excitation.
(d) excessive grid bias.
(e) an insufficient audio signal from the modulator.

(a) I I   (b) I I   (c) I I   (d) I I   (e) I I

46. For carrier frequencies between 25 and 50 MHz, the maximum authorized bandwidth for Public Safety Radio stations in FM service is:
(a) 150 kHz   (b) 30 kHz   (c) 20 kHz
(d) 10 kHz   (e) 5 kHz

(a) I I   (b) I I   (c) I I   (d) I I   (e) I I

47. When a transmission line is terminated by a resistive load equal to the surge impedance, the:
(a) line carries only standing waves.
(b) VSWR = 0.
(c) reflection coefficient is unity.
(d) power dissipated in the load is equal to the power dissipated in the line.

(e) input impedance of the line at the generator end equals the surge impedance of the line.

(a) I I   (b) I I   (c) I I   (d) I I   (e) I I

48. A disadvantage of a tuned radio frequency (TRF) receiver is:
(a) poor selectivity at high frequencies.
(b) poor sensitivity at high frequencies.
(c) that it requires a beat frequency oscillator to demodulate telephony.
(d) its unsuitability for strong signals.
(e) Both (a) and (b) are true.

(a) I I   (b) I I   (c) I I   (d) I I   (e) I I

49. An interstage audio transformer has a center-tapped secondary. This may be used to:
(a) feed a class AB_1 single tube amplifier.
(b) feed two parallel tubes operated in class A.
(c) feed a class A cathode follower.
(d) provide two 180° out-of-phase signals for a push-pull amplifier input.
(e) provide two in-phase signals for a push-pull amplifier.

(a) I I   (b) I I   (c) I I   (d) I I   (e) I I

50. Positive feedback with the Armstrong oscillator occurs through the:
(a) plate to grid interelectrode capacitance.
(b) plate to cathode interelectrode capacitance.
(c) grid to cathode interelectrode capacitance.
(d) mutual inductance between the grid and the plate coils.
(e) inductive feedback across a tapped coil.

(a) I I   (b) I I   (c) I I   (d) I I   (e) I I

51. The dc output voltage from a single-phase bridge rectifier has a ripple frequency equal to:
(a) the source frequency.
(b) that from a half-wave rectifier.
(c) twice the source frequency.
(d) that from a three-phase full-wave rectifier.
(e) Both (a) and (b) are true.

(a) I I   (b) I I   (c) I I   (d) I I   (e) I I

52. If a pure inductor, resistor and capacitor are connected in parallel and are at resonance:
(a) the power factor is one.
(b) the power factor is zero.
(c) all currents are in phase.
(d) the supply voltage and the supply current are 90° out of phase.
(e) the impedance is a minimum.

(a) I I   (b) I I   (c) I I   (d) I I   (e) I I

53. Twenty kilowatts is equal to:
(a) 2000 W   (b) 20,000,000 mW

(c) 0.2 MW   (d) 0.002 MW
(e) 2,000,000,000 μ W

(a) | | (b) | | (c) | | (d) | | (e) | |

54. Which of the following circuits can uti-
lize an audio signal to control the frequency
shift of an RF oscillator?
(a) The phasitron.
(b) The reactance-tube circuit.
(c) The phantastron.
(d) The ratio detector.
(e) The Foster-Seeley discriminator.

(a) | | (b) | | (c) | | (d) | | (e) | |

55. The antenna current meter of an FM
transmitter reads 5 A when 50% modulated.
What will the ammeter read with no modulation?
(a) 22.5% decrease in its original value.
(b) 33 1/3% decrease in its original value.
(c) 18.5% increase in its original value.
(d) 50% decrease in its original value.
(e) The reading would not change.

(a) | | (b) | | (c) | | (d) | | (e) | |

56. In Public Safety Radio Services, the
mean power of emissions shall be attenuated
below the mean output power of the transmitter on any frequency removed from the assigned frequency by more than 100% up to
and including 250% of the authorized bandwidth, such attenuation being by at least:
(a) 10 dB   (b) 20 dB   (c) 25 dB
(d) 35 dB   (e) 80 dB

(a) | | (b) | | (c) | | (d) | | (e) | |

57. A quarter-wave Marconi antenna which
is resonant at 7 MHz is operated at 21 MHz.
The antenna load will be:
(a) inductive.   (b) capacitive.
(c) a high impedance. (d) a low resistance.
(e) None of the above are true.

(a) | | (b) | | (c) | | (d) | | (e) | |

58. Space diversity reception:
(a) has the same signal sent on two or more
     frequencies to overcome the effects of
     fading with skywave propagation.
(b) is used on UHF for direction-finding
     purposes.
(c) uses a number of antennas which are fed
     by the same signal with different phase
     relationships to achieve a unidirectional
     radiation pattern.
(d) uses two or more receiving antennas
     (and receivers) that are spaced several
     wavelengths apart to overcome the ef-
     fects of propagation fading.
(e) cannot be used to receive signals from a
     fixed station.

(a) | | (b) | | (c) | | (d) | | (e) | |

59. An amplifier tube has an ac plate resistance of 8,000 ohms. For a small signal

input, the power output will be a maximum
when the load resistor equals:
(a) 8 kohms.   (b) 16 kohms.
(c) 4 kohms.   (d) 24 kohms.
(e) 80 kohms.

(a) | | (b) | | (c) | | (d) | | (e) | |

60. What is the name of the basic moving
coil meter movement?
(a) Marconi.   (b) Bellini-Tosi.
(c) d'Arsonval.   (d) Tesla.
(e) Hertz.

(a) | | (b) | | (c) | | (d) | | (e) | |

61. The main advantage of the mercury-
vapor rectifier over the hard diode rectifier
is:
(a) the increased space charge effect.
(b) due to the fact that there is no require-
     ment for a warm-up period.
(c) the lower internal voltage drop.
(d) the increased peak inverse voltage.
(e) due to the fact that it does not create RF
     interference.

(a) | | (b) | | (c) | | (d) | | (e) | |

62. The efficiency of a power transformer
is equal to 100% times the quotient of the:
(a) secondary voltage divided by the primary
     voltage.
(b) primary current divided by the secon-
     dary current.
(c) power in the primary circuit divided by
     the power in the secondary circuit.
(d) power in the secondary circuit divided
     by the power in the primary circuit.
(e) None of these but frequently less than
     70%.

(a) | | (b) | | (c) | | (d) | | (e) | |

63. In the circuit shown in Fig. 3, what is
the battery voltage:
(a) 12 V   (b) 16 V   (c) 20 V
(d) 8 V   (e) 36 V

(a) | | (b) | | (c) | | (d) | | (e) | |

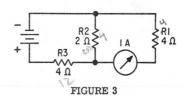

FIGURE 3

64. With an increase in temperature affecting the circuit shown in Fig. 4, the effect of
RT_1 will:
(a) increase the static collector current.
(b) cause the quiescent base current to
     increase.
(c) cause the static emitter current to in-
     crease.
(d) increase the static base current.

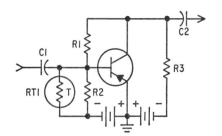

FIGURE 4

(e) tend to stabilize the quiescent collector current.

(a) I I   (b) I I   (c) I I   (d) I I   (e) I I

65. The schematic shown in Fig. 5 represents a rectifier unit suitable for a transmitter power supply. The circuit as shown is operating correctly. If fuse F2 blows, which of the following is a possible cause?
(a) L2 is an open circuit.
(b) R2 is an open circuit.
(c) R3 is an open circuit.
(d) L1 is a short circuit.
(e) C6 is a short circuit.

(a) I I   (b) I I   (c) I I   (d) I I   (e) I I

66. In the schematic of Fig. 5, if C5 becomes open, which of the following results would occur?
(a) All the dc voltages would be changed.
(b) The +150 and +70 voltages would fall to zero.
(c) The percentage regulation would increase.
(d) The output voltages would contain more ripple.
(e) The +280 voltage would increase.

(a) I I   (b) I I   (c) I I   (d) I I   (e) I I

67. If in the schematic of Fig. 5, all of the dc output voltages fall to zero, which of the following is a possible cause?
(a) A short across L1.
(b) A short across L2.
(c) R1 is an open circuit.
(d) R2 is an open circuit.
(e) R3 is an open circuit.

(a) I I   (b) I I   (c) I I   (d) I I   (e) I I

68. If in the schematic of Fig. 5 R1 is open, which of the following would occur?
(a) The percentage regulation would increase.
(b) The ripple percentage would increase.
(c) The power supply would operate normally.
(d) Fuse F2 would blow.
(e) The output voltage would increase.

(a) I I   (b) I I   (c) I I   (d) I I   (e) I I

69. If in the schematic of Fig. 5, C6 is an open circuit, which of the following would occur?
(a) The dc output voltages would fall to zero.
(b) The percentage of regulation would fall.
(c) Fuse F2 would blow.
(d) The output ripple voltage would increase.
(e) Both (b) and (d) are true.

(a) I I   (b) I I   (c) I I   (d) I I   (e) I I

70. If in the schematic of Fig. 5 C1 is an open circuit, which of the following would occur?
(a) An increase of possible RF interference to the supply would exist.
(b) The primary would no longer present a balanced load to the 120 V supply.
(c) The primary would no longer be protected from current surges when the power supply is turned on.

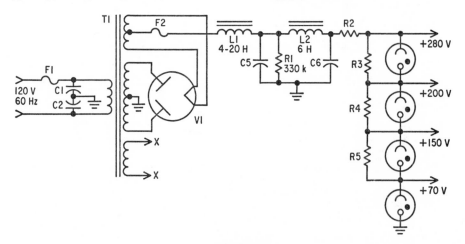

FIGURE 5

(d) Ripple frequency harmonics could feed back to the 120 V supply.
(e) Any frequency drift in the 120 V supply could enter the power supply.

(a) I I   (b) I I   (c) I I   (d) I I   (e) I I

71. If in the schematic of Fig. 5 fuse F1 blows, which of the following is a possible cause?
(a) A short circuit across the heater filament of the rectifier tube.
(b) An open circuit in the filament of the rectifier tube.
(c) A short across L1.
(d) A short across R2.
(e) A short across L2.

(a) I I   (b) I I   (c) I I   (d) I I   (e) I I

72. If in the schematic of Fig. 5 L1 is shorted across the coil, which of the following would occur?
(a) The dc output voltages would fall to zero.
(b) The percentage regulation would be decreased.
(c) Fuse F2 would blow.
(d) Resistor R1 would burn out.
(e) None of the above are true.

(a) I I   (b) I I   (c) I I   (d) I I   (e) I I

73. The positive plate of an Edison storage cell is composed of what active chemical composition?
(a) Potassium hydroxide.   (b) Soft lead.
(c) Nickel and nickel hydrate.
(d) Iron oxide.   (e) Lead sulphate.

(a) I I   (b) I I   (c) I I   (d) I I   (e) I I

74. The position of an antenna with respect to the surface of the earth:
(a) does not affect the received signal.
(b) does not affect the transmitted wave.
(c) determines the polarization of the emitted wave.
(d) determines its efficiency as an RF radiator.
(e) is unimportant.

(a) I I   (b) I I   (c) I I   (d) I I   (e) I I

75. The feedback from the plate circuit of a triode to the grid circuit in the grounded cathode configuration:
(a) is associated with the interelectrode capacitance between the control grid and plate.
(b) may be degenerative under certain circuit conditions.
(c) may be regenerative under certain circuit conditions.
(d) can be counteracted by neutralization.
(e) All of the above are true.

(a) I I   (b) I I   (c) I I   (d) I I   (e) I I

76. Which of the following characteristics describes the properties of a class A amplifier?

(a) Grid current flows for a portion of the input cycle.
(b) The tube is biased to projected cut-off.
(c) High plate efficiency.
(d) Minimum output signal distortion compared to other classes of amplifiers.
(e) Very high power gain as compared to other classes of amplifiers.

(a) I I   (b) I I   (c) I I   (d) I I   (e) I I

77. The space charge in a pentode is mainly between the:
(a) screen grid and control grid.
(b) plate and suppressor grid.
(c) control grid and cathode.
(d) screen and suppressor grids.
(e) None of the above are true.

(a) I I   (b) I I   (c) I I   (d) I I   (e) I I

78. A component may be shielded from a unidirectional magnetic field by using:
(a) an aluminum can.
(b) a Faraday screen.
(c) a soft iron shield.
(d) a screen of low dielectric constant.
(e) a screen of high permittivity.

(a) I I   (b) I I   (c) I I   (d) I I   (e) I I

79. An ac circuit that is not in resonance contains a resistor, an inductor and a capacitor in series. Which of the following phase relationships is true?
(a) The inductor voltage and capacitor voltage are 90° out of phase.
(b) The resistor voltage and current are 180° out of phase.
(c) The source voltage and resistor voltage are in phase.
(d) The resistor voltage lags the inductor voltage by 90°.
(e) The capacitor voltage leads the resistor voltage by 90°.

(a) I I   (b) I I   (c) I I   (d) I I   (e) I I

80. A 0.2H inductor is wound with 2000 turns of wire. If an additional 500 turns are added without changing the length of the coil, the new inductance would become (approximately):
(a) 0.25 H   (b) 0.27 H   (c) 0.31 H
(d) 0.34 H   (e) 0.37 H

(a) I I   (b) I I   (c) I I   (d) I I   (e) I I

81. In the operation of a transistor amplifier, the:
(a) forward bias of a class A amplifier is less than the forward bias of a class B amplifier.
(b) forward bias of a class B amplifier is less than the forward bias of a class C amplifier.
(c) forward bias of a class A amplifier is greater than the forward bias of a class B amplifier.

(d) forward bias of a class C amplifier is greater than the forward bias of a class B amplifier.
(e) Both (a) and (b) are true.

(a)|l   (b)|l   (c)|l   (d)|l   (e)|l

82. A balanced modulator may be found in:
(a) a high-level modulated AM transmitter.
(b) an AM transmitter that is crystal-controlled.
(c) a low-level modulated AM transmitter using frequency multipliers.
(d) a VHF AM transmitter using an AFC system.
(e) a single-sideband transmitter with suppressed carrier.

(a)|l   (b)|l   (c)|l   (d)|l   (e)|l

83. A waveguide is:
(a) a rectangular or round metal tube.
(b) easier to install and operate than a co-axial line.
(c) used at radio frequencies below 50 MHz.
(d) inversely proportional in size to the wavelength used.
(e) unable to transmit higher power than a coaxial line of the same size.

(a)|l   (b)|l   (c)|l   (d)|l   (e)|l

84. Propagation fading may be due to:
(a) combining of the sky and ground waves at the receiver.
(b) irregular variations of ionization density in the ionosphere.
(c) sky wave arriving at the receiver after reflections from different layers.
(d) sky wave arriving at the receiver after a number of reflections and hops between the earth and ionosphere.
(e) All the above are true.

(a)|l   (b)|l   (c)|l   (d)|l   (e)|l

85. By mistake an operator is attempting to receive a standard broadcast transmission when his band-pass switch is set to the CW position. The BFO is inoperative. The result would be that:
(a) only noise would be heard.
(b) the broadcast signal would be entirely eliminated.
(c) the broadcast signal would blast the loudspeaker.
(d) the broadcast signal would be very weak but undistorted.
(e) the broadcast signal would be badly distorted.

(a)|l   (b)|l   (c)|l   (d)|l   (e)|l

86. Amplitude or nonlinear distortion in audio amplifiers may be caused by:
(a) negative feedback.
(b) driving the grid to cut-off.
(c) lack of grid current flow.

(d) operation on the nonlinear portion of the tube characteristic curve.
(e) Both (b) and (d) are true.

(a)|l   (b)|l   (c)|l   (d)|l   (e)|l

87. Plate to control grid capacitance is reduced to a very low value in:
(a) triodes.   (b) tetrodes.
(c) pentodes.   (d) beam power tubes.
(e) Both (b) and (c) are true.

(a)|l   (b)|l   (c)|l   (d)|l   (e)|l

88. In an ac circuit that is inductive, the:
(a) power factor is greater than 1.
(b) current lags the voltage.
(c) current leads the voltage.
(d) voltage lags the current.
(e) true power is greater than the apparent power.

(a)|l   (b)|l   (c)|l   (d)|l   (e)|l

89. If the RMS value of a sine wave ac is 15 V, the peak to peak value is:
(a) 21.2 V   (b) 42.4 V   (c) 31 V
(d) 10.5 V   (e) 62 V

(a)|l   (b)|l   (c)|l   (d)|l   (e)|l

90. A break contact relay has:
(a) points that make contact when the coil is energized.
(b) contact points that are normally closed.
(c) points that make contact when the coil is de-energized.
(d) contact points that are normally open.
(e) Both (b) and (c) are correct.

(a)|l   (b)|l   (c)|l   (d)|l   (e)|l

91. The input ac voltage to a voltage doubler rectifier circuit is 200 V. The no-load output voltage is approximately:
(a) 800 V   (b) 566 V   (c) 433 V
(d) 283 V   (e) 100 V

(a)|l   (b)|l   (c)|l   (d)|l   (e)|l

92. In which of the following transmitters (or receivers) is "pre-emphasis" used?
(a) Phase-modulated transmitters.
(b) Frequency-modulated transmitters.
(c) AM receivers.
(d) FM receivers.
(e) Both (a) and (b) are true.

(a)|l   (b)|l   (c)|l   (d)|l   (e)|l

93. The bandwidth of a traveling-wave tube is wide because:
(a) it is inherently a nonresonant device.
(b) it uses a resonant cavity with a low Q.
(c) the helix is used to frequency modulate the electron beam.
(d) multiple resonant cavities are used that are stagger tuned to produce the wide bandwidth.
(e) the attenuator spreads out the bandwidth.

(a)|l   (b)|l   (c)|l   (d)|l   (e)|l

94. At the feed point of a resonant center fed one-half wave Hertz dipole, the:
(a) voltage is a maximum.
(b) current is a minimum.
(c) antenna impedance is 35 ohms.
(d) current is a maximum.
(e) antenna impedance is 150 ohms.

(a) I I   (b) I I   (c) I I   (d) I I   (e) I I

95. It is intended to completely align a double conversion FM receiver. The first stage to be aligned would usually be the:
(a) noise suppression circuit.
(b) discriminator.
(c) last high IF stage.
(d) second local oscillator.
(e) first low IF stage.

(a) I I   (b) I I   (c) I I   (d) I I   (e) I I

96. A class B push-pull audio amplifier has a plate efficiency of approximately:
(a) 25%   (b) 50%   (c) 78.5%
(d) 85%   (e) 10%

(a) I I   (b) I I   (c) I I   (d) I I   (e) I I

97. To convert a milliammeter into a voltmeter:
(a) add a high value resistor across the meter movement.
(b) add a low value resistor in parallel with the meter movement.
(c) add a resistor in series with the meter movement.
(d) add a resistor in series with the meter movement and another resistor in parallel with the meter movement.
(e) No conversion is required. The milliammeter may always be connected directly across the voltage to be measured.

(a) I I   (b) I I   (c) I I   (d) I I   (e) I I

98. An advantage of a half-wave rectifier over a full-wave rectifier is:
(a) easier filtering.
(b) better regulation.
(c) a higher dc output voltage for a given transformer secondary voltage.
(d) the higher fundamental frequency of the ripple.
(e) Both (a) and (b) are true.

(a) I I   (b) I I   (c) I I   (d) I I   (e) I I

99. An audio transformer which will match a 10 kohm source to a 4 ohm speaker requires a turns ratio of:
(a) 2500 to 1   (b) 1 to 2500
(c) 50 to 1   (d) 6,250,000 to 1
(e) 7.07 to 1

(a) I I   (b) I I   (c) I I   (d) I I   (e) I I

100. An inductor of 0.5 H and containing 1000 turns is rewound with 2000 turns without altering the coil's length. The new inductance will be:
(a) 0.25 H   (b) 0.5 H   (c) 1 H
(d) 2 H   (e) 4 H

(a) I I   (b) I I   (c) I I   (d) I I   (e) I I

Element 3, Test 8

1. In the common emitter amplifier, current feedback is eliminated by:
(a) using "boot strap" bias for the base.
(b) operating the transistor such that the collector and base are 180° out of phase with each other.
(c) using two batteries instead of one for the power source.
(d) by-passing the emitter stabilizing resistor.
(e) This is an erroneous statement. Current feedback cannot be eliminated in this circuit.

(a) I I   (b) I I   (c) I I   (d) I I   (e) I I

2. The frequency tolerance of a Public Safety Radio Services mobile station of more than 3 W while operating between the frequencies of 470 and 512 MHz is:
(a) 0.001%   (b) 0.002%   (c) 0.003%
(d) 0.005%   (e) 0.0005%

(a) I I   (b) I I   (c) I I   (d) I I   (e) I I

3. The plane of polarization of an electromagnetic wave is:
(a) defined by the direction of the electric field and the direction of propagation.
(b) defined by the direction of the magnetic field and the direction of propagation.
(c) perpendicular to the plane defined by the direction of the electric field and the direction of propagation.
(d) determined by the physical placement of the transmitter's antenna.
(e) Both (a) and (d) are true.

(a) I I   (b) I I   (c) I I   (d) I I   (e) I I

4. Parasitic oscillations in an RF power amplifier which has been correctly tuned:
(a) may often be found with a neon indicator.
(b) can result in the radiation of spurious sidebands during modulation.
(c) can be reduced by connecting a low value resistor in series with the control grid.
(d) can be reduced by connecting the parallel combination of a small value resistor and an inductor in series with the plate and control-grid leads.
(e) All of the above are true.

(a) I I   (b) I I   (c) I I   (d) I I   (e) I I

5. An advantage of an electron-coupled oscillator is:
(a) that the output plate circuit is isolated from the oscillator circuitry.
(b) that no buffer is required.
(c) its good frequency stability.
(d) that frequency multiplication is possible between the grid and the plate circuits.
(e) All of the above are true.

(a) I I   (b) I I   (c) I I   (d) I I   (e) I I

6. An audio pentode amplifier has a grid bias of -6 V with an input signal of 3V RMS. The screen grid voltage is 250 V and the peak-to-peak voltage swing on the plate is 240 V. What is the amplifier's voltage gain?
(a) 80   (b) 40   (c) 36   (d) 28
(e) 18

(a) I I   (b) I I   (c) I I   (d) I I   (e) I I

7. In a series LCR circuit, the inductive reactance is greater than the capacitive reactance. The result is that the:
(a) current leads the source voltage.
(b) source voltage lags the current.
(c) power factor is greater than 1.
(d) circuit current lags the source voltage.
(e) voltage across the inductor and the voltage across the capacitor are 90° out of phase.

(a) I I   (b) I I   (c) I I   (d) I I   (e) I I

8. A short develops across the filter capacitor in a full-wave rectifier circuit. The result is that:
(a) the dc output voltage will fall to zero.
(b) the primary fuse will blow if no secondary fuse is present.
(c) the rectifier plates may become red hot.
(d) if present, the secondary fuse will blow.
(e) each of the above is a true statement.

(a) I I   (b) I I   (c) I I   (d) I I   (e) I I

9. When carrier shift exists in an AM transmitter, it is not likely to be caused by:
(a) a poorly regulated modulator power supply.
(b) insufficient modulation.
(c) overmodulation.
(d) improper neutralization.
(e) improper amplifier tuning.

(a) | | (b) | | (c) | | (d) | | (e) | |

10. The deviation ratio of Public Safety Radio Services two-way mobile communications frequency-modulated systems operating between 25 and 470 MHz is:
(a) 1.667   (b) 2.0   (c) 5.0   (d) 75
(e) 85

(a) | | (b) | | (c) | | (d) | | (e) | |

11. What is the input impedance of a quarter wavelength section of transmission line that is shorted at one end?
(a) Zero.
(b) A very high value of resistance.
(c) Equal to the surge impedance.
(d) Equal to half the surge impedance.
(e) None of the above are true.

(a) | | (b) | | (c) | | (d) | | (e) | |

12. If the grid bias of an amplifier is such that plate current flows for 120^0 to 150^0 of the input signal's 360^0 cycle, the stage is said to be operating in:
(a) class AB1.   (b) class C.
(c) class B.   (d) class AB2.
(e) class A.

(a) | | (b) | | (c) | | (d) | | (e) | |

13. Which of the following oscillator circuits uses mutual coupling between separate plate and grid coils?
(a) Pierce.   (b) Armstrong.
(c) Hartley.   (d) Miller.
(e) Colpitts.

(a) | | (b) | | (c) | | (d) | | (e) | |

14. The term "physical length" as referred to a Marconi antenna means:
(a) the actual length of an antenna cut to resonate in the half wavelength mode.
(b) the distance the wave will travel on the antenna during one half of a period.
(c) a quarter wavelength in free space.
(d) the actual length of an antenna cut to resonate in the quarter wavelength mode.

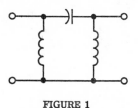

FIGURE 1

(e) multiplying a quarter wavelength in free space by 1.707.

(a) | | (b) | | (c) | | (d) | | (e) | |

15. The circuit shown in Fig. 1 represents a:
(a) band-pass π section filter.
(b) high-pass π section filter.
(c) low-pass π section filter.
(d) high-pass T section filter.
(e) high-pass L section filter.

(a) | | (b) | | (c) | | (d) | | (e) | |

16. A phase splitter is used to:
(a) provide, from a single input signal, two output signals that are 90^0 out of phase.
(b) couple a push-push amplifier to a single-tube amplifier.
(c) couple a single-tube amplifier to a push-pull amplifier.
(d) convert a single-phase supply to a three-phase supply.
(e) couple a single-tube amplifier to an amplifier operating with two tubes in parallel.

(a) | | (b) | | (c) | | (d) | | (e) | |

17. A "flow of holes" in semiconductor material refers to a flow of:
(a) positive carriers.   (b) negative carriers.
(c) donor atoms.   (d) neutrons.
(e) acceptor atoms.

(a) | | (b) | | (c) | | (d) | | (e) | |

18. A "Base Station" is defined as a:
(a) land station in the land mobile service carrying on a service with land mobile stations.
(b) land station in the maritime mobile service.
(c) station in the earth-space service, located either on the earth's surface or on an object which is limited to flight between points on the earth's surface.
(d) station in the fixed service.
(e) station in the mobile service not intended to be used while in motion.

(a) | | (b) | | (c) | | (d) | | (e) | |

19. Along a transmission line, a voltage antinode is measured at 20 V with an adjacent node of 10 V. The voltage standing wave ratio is:
(a) 2 to 1   (b) 1/2 to 1
(c) 4 to 1   (d) 1/4 to 1
(e) It cannot be found from the information given.

(a) | | (b) | | (c) | | (d) | | (e) | |

20. An RF doubler stage would not employ:
(a) beam power tubes.
(b) pentode tubes.
(c) triode tubes.
(d) a push-pull arrangement.
(e) Both (c) and (d) are true.

(a) | | (b) | | (c) | | (d) | | (e) | |

21. A square wave may be used to test the frequency response of an audio amplifier if the output is viewed on an oscilloscope because the:
(a) square wave cannot drive the amplifier into distortion.
(b) resultant waveshape indicates the frequency response.
(c) harmonics do not exceed the fourth.
(d) square wave can drive the control grid above zero and beyond cut-off to create harmonic distortion.
(e) Both (a) and (b) are true.

(a) I I   (b) I I   (c) I I   (d) I I   (e) I I

22. The symbol shown in Fig. 2 represents a:
(a) VR tube.
(b) grounded-grid triode tube.
(c) lighthouse triode tube.
(d) high-power, forced-air-cooled triode tube.
(e) thyratron tube.

(a) I I   (b) I I   (c) I I   (d) I I   (e) I I

FIGURE 2

23. Skin effect:
(a) causes an increase in a conductor's effective resistance at radio frequencies.
(b) causes an increase in a conductor's inductance at radio frequencies.
(c) is reduced to a low level in Litz wire.
(d) causes ionization of the air at the surface of conductors carrying high voltages.
(e) Both (a) and (c) are true.

(a) I I   (b) I I   (c) I I   (d) I I   (e) I I

24. The impedance of a high Q parallel resonant tank circuit is equal to:
(a) C/LR ohms.
(b) Q multiplied by the RF resistance of the coil.
(c) Q multiplied by the reactance of the capacitor.
(d) the reactance of the inductor divided by Q.
(e) the RF resistance of the coil.

(a) I I   (b) I I   (c) I I   (d) I I   (e) I I

25. The reactance tube method of producing FM:
(a) can only be used in high-level modulation of the final RF stage.
(b) can never be used if frequency multiplication is achieved in the RF stages.
(c) causes a standard tube to behave as an inductive or capacitive reactance, whose value is controlled by an audio signal.

(d) is a phase-modulation method in which sidebands are shifted by 90° and then combined with the carrier.
(e) uses a phasitron tube in conjunction with an audio correction network.

(a) I I   (b) I I   (c) I I   (d) I I   (e) I I

26. The output voltage of a dc generator is 550 V under load and 620 V under no load. What is the voltage regulation of the generator?
(a) 10.7%   (b) 11.3%   (c) 12.7%
(d) 15.0%   (e) 20.0%

(a) I I   (b) I I   (c) I I   (d) I I   (e) I I

27. One advantage of the ratio detector over the Foster-Seeley discriminator is that the ratio detector:
(a) can also be used for AM.
(b) is easier to align.
(c) limits the amplitude modulation contained in the signal.
(d) has greater linearity.
(e) is more sensitive.

(a) I I   (b) I I   (c) I I   (d) I I   (e) I I

28. If the gain of an amplifier is 40 dB with equal input and output impedances, the ratio of output voltage to input voltage is:
(a) 20   (b) 40   (c) 100   (d) 200
(e) 1000

(a) I I   (b) I I   (c) I I   (d) I I   (e) I I

29. The inductance of a swinging choke varies with the load current. This variation in inductance is achieved by:
(a) reducing the number of turns.
(b) using iron rather than copper wire.
(c) providing a small air gap between the core's laminations.
(d) using thicker laminations for the iron core.
(e) None of the above are true.

(a) I I   (b) I I   (c) I I   (d) I I   (e) I I

30. An ac sine-wave voltage has a frequency of 60 Hz and its peak-to-peak value is 100 V. What is its effective voltage?
(a) 35.35 V   (b) 50.0 V   (c) 63.6 V
(d) 70.7 V   (e) 141.4 V

(a) I I   (b) I I   (c) I I   (d) I I   (e) I I

31. Two 0.02 μ F capacitors are connected in series across a 150 V dc source. The source is then removed and replaced by a third 0.02 μ F capacitor that was originally uncharged. What is the voltage across the third capacitor?
(a) 25 V   (b) 50 V   (c) 75 V
(d) 100 V   (e) 125 V

(a) I I   (b) I I   (c) I I   (d) I I   (e) I I

32. In a frequency modulated transmitter, the audio modulating frequency is 2.5 kHz

and there are eight significant upper sidebands. What is the bandwidth of the emission?
(a) 2.5 kHz   (b) 5.0 kHz
(c) 40.0 kHz   (d) 80.0 kHz
(e) 200 kHz

(a) I I   (b) I I   (c) I I   (d) I I   (e) I I

33. The dynamotor has an approximate efficiency of:
(a) 50%   (b) 30%   (c) 25%   (d) 70%
(e) 40%

(a) I I   (b) I I   (c) I I   (d) I I   (e) I I

34. The circuit shown in Fig. 3 represents:
(a) a phase-conscious rectifier.
(b) a bridge modulator.
(c) an FM discriminator.
(d) a noise limiter.
(e) a ratio detector.

(a) I I   (b) I I   (c) I I   (d) I I   (e) I I

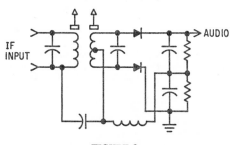

FIGURE 3

35. A cathode follower stage:
(a) has a low input impedance.
(b) has a high output impedance.
(c) has a high voltage gain.
(d) has no phase change between the input
    signal on the grid and the output signal
    from the cathode.
(e) is equivalent to a common base stage.

(a) I I   (b) I I   (c) I I   (d) I I   (e) I I

36. Which of the following types of rectifiers
is a possible cause of radio-frequency interference?
(a) The high vacuum diode.
(b) The mercury vapor diode.
(c) The copper-oxide rectifier.
(d) The SCR.
(e) The selenium diode.

(a) I I   (b) I I   (c) I I   (d) I I   (e) I I

37. An RF amplifier uses a high Q tank circuit as its plate load. A high value resistor
is connected across the tank circuit. As a
result:
(a) the impedance of the plate load would
    decrease and therefore its resonant fre-
    quency would increase.
(b) the change in Q would cause the resonant
    frequency of the plate load to decrease.

(c) the resonant frequency of the plate load
    would remain unchanged.
(d) the amplifier's gain would increase in
    conjunction with the rise in Q.
(e) the amplifier could break into self-oscil-
    lation.

(a) I I   (b) I I   (c) I I   (d) I I   (e) I I

38. If a dc circuit dissipates 125 W, what
will be the energy consumed in one day?
(a) 125 W   (b) 3000 W   (c) 30 kWh
(d) 300 W-hr   (e) 3 kWh

(a) I I   (b) I I   (c) I I   (d) I I   (e) I I

39. If the amplitude of an FM modulating
audio signal is kept constant but the frequency
is lowered, the result is:
(a) a greater number of significant sidebands.
(b) an increased spacing between sidebands
    and therefore a greater bandwidth.
(c) a greater degree of pre-emphasis.
(d) a lower value of modulation index.
(e) an increase in carrier amplitude.

(a) I I   (b) I I   (c) I I   (d) I I   (e) I I

40. The voltage output can be varied in a
separately excited ac generator by:
(a) changing the brush position.
(b) varying the frequency of the excitation
    voltage.
(c) using a variable capacitor across the
    field.
(d) using a governor.
(e) varying the current in the field.

(a) I I   (b) I I   (c) I I   (d) I I   (e) I I

41. During modulation, frequency shift in a
transmitter can be produced by:
(a) using excessive plate and screen voltages
    in the output stage.
(b) overmodulation.
(c) using poorly regulated power supplies.
(d) using frequency multipliers.
(e) lack of crystal control.

(a) I I   (b) I I   (c) I I   (d) I I   (e) I I

42. A triode audio amplifier tube operates
with a μ of 25. The plate supply voltage is
250 V, the plate current is 8 mA and the
cathode resistor is 680 ohms. The grid bias
voltage providing class A operation is:
(a) -10 V   (b) -3.125 V   (c) -8.5 V
(d) -5.44 V   (e) -2.38 V

(a) I I   (b) I I   (c) I I   (d) I I   (e) I I

43. The no-load output voltage from a power
supply is 500 V while the full-load voltage is
450 V. What is the percentage regulation?
(a) 100%   (b) 50%   (c) 45%   (d) 11%
(e) 9%

(a) I I   (b) I I   (c) I I   (d) I I   (e) I I

44. A bleeder resistor is in parallel with a
8 μ F filter capacitor rated at 500 V. The dc

output voltage is 400 V and the bleeder current is 20 mA. The bleeder power dissipation is:
(a) 80 W   (b) 80 VA   (c) 8 W
(d) 10 W   (e) 16 W

(a) I I   (b) I I   (c) I I   (d) I I   (e) I I

45. What is the total power in the circuit shown in Fig. 4?
(a) 20 W   (b) 10 W   (c) 5 W
(d) 1 W   (e) 0.1 W

(a) I I   (b) I I   (c) I I   (d) I I   (e) I I

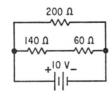

FIGURE 4

46. A class A triode audio amplifier stage uses cathode bias. If the cathode bypass capacitor becomes open:
(a) there will be regenerative feedback and the danger of self-oscillation will exist.
(b) the bias will drop to zero.
(c) motorboating may occur.
(d) frequency distortion will be reduced.
(e) amplitude distortion will increase.

(a) I I   (b) I I   (c) I I   (d) I I   (e) I I

47. With plate modulation, using a pentode tube, the reason for modulating both the screen grid and the plate is that:
(a) varying the plate voltage has little effect on the plate current.
(b) at the trough of the modulation cycle, the screen grid current would be excessive unless the screen grid is modulated.
(c) modulating the screen grid prevents saturation of the plate current.
(d) modulating the screen grid prevents excessive plate current at the peak of the modulating cycle.
(e) modulating the screen grid prevents carrier shift in the modulation envelope of the AM wave.

(a) I I   (b) I I   (c) I I   (d) I I   (e) I I

48. When the magnetic field is parallel to the direction of the signal propagation in the waveguide and the electric field is at right angles to the direction of propagation, the mode of operation is:
(a) TE mode.   (b) ET mode.
(c) MT mode.   (d) TM mode.
(e) None of the above are true.

(a) I I   (b) I I   (c) I I   (d) I I   (e) I I

49. Insulators are inserted into antenna guy wires to:

(a) increase the RF losses in the guy wires so that they will not conduct.
(b) improve the transmitter loading.
(c) decrease the dc resistance of the guy wires.
(d) reduce the possibility of the guy wires acting as efficient radiators.
(e) increase the electrical length of the antenna.

(a) I I   (b) I I'   (c) I I   (d) I I   (e) I I

50. Which of the following has the lowest plate efficiency?
(a) Class A.   (b) Class AB_1.
(c) Class AB_2.   (d) Class B.
(e) Class C.

(a) I I   (b) I I   (c) I I   (d) I I   (e) I I

51. Power consumed in a circuit is measured by:
(a) a wattmeter.   (b) a voltmeter.
(c) an electroscope.   (d) an ammeter.
(e) a watt-hour meter.

(a) I I   (b) I I   (c) I I   (d) I I   (e) I I

52. The secondary of a power transformer supplies a current of 10 A. If the secondary becomes an open circuit, the primary current would:
(a) blow the fuse in the primary circuit.
(b) drop to zero.
(c) remain unchanged.
(d) greatly decrease.
(e) saturate the core.

(a) I I   (b) I I   (c) I I   (d) I I   (e) I I

53. A load which is operated from a 6 V dc source is found to be dissipating 15 W. What is the current drawn from the source?
(a) 2.5 A   (b) 2.0 A   (c) 2.1 A
(d) 0.4 A   (e) 90 A

(a) I I   (b) I I   (c) I I   (d) I I   (e) I I

54. If the feedback applied to a crystal becomes excessive, the result may be:
(a) normal operation.
(b) a reduced bias.
(c) a fractured crystal.
(d) that the crystal will overheat.
(e) Both (c) and (d) are true.

(a) I I   (b) I I   (c) I I   (d) I I   (e) I I

55. If a 5 kHz tone is used to amplitude modulate a 1 MHz carrier:
(a) sideband frequencies of 1000.5 and 999.5 kHz are produced.
(b) the total bandwidth of the modulated signal is 5 kHz.
(c) frequencies of 5 kHz, 1 MHz, 999.5 kHz and 1,000.5 kHz are radiated from the antenna.
(d) the upper sideband has a frequency of 1005 kHz and the lower sideband a frequency of 995 kHz.

(e) for 100% modulation, the power in the upper sideband is 50% of the unmodulated carrier power.

(a) l l   (b) l l   (c) l l   (d) l l   (e) l l

56. A waveguide may be:
(a) referred to as a coaxial cable.
(b) referred to as a concentric cable.
(c) a hollow metal tube with a smooth interior.
(d) a central conductor inside a round pipe.
(e) a hollow metal tube with dielectric spacers and dry air inside.

(a) l l   (b) l l   (c) l l   (d) l l   (e) l l

57. In an RF oscillator stage using a pentode, electrons flow from (through):
(a) the screen grid to the plate.
(b) the screen grid to the positive terminal of the screen grid supply voltage.
(c) the control grid to the ground through the grid leak resistor.
(d) the ground to the cathode.
(e) All the above are true.

(a) l l   (b) l l   (c) l l   (d) l l   (e) l l

58. Which of the diagrams in Fig. 5 correctly show the voltage and current distribution in a Marconi antenna?

(a) l l   (b) l l   (c) l l   (d) l l   (e) l l

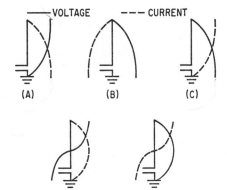

FIGURE 5

59. Vacuum-tube voltmeters:
(a) have a low input impedance.
(b) can be used to measure small currents in the order of microamps.
(c) cannot be used to measure high resistances.
(d) do not require a power supply.
(e) use two tubes in a balanced-bridge circuit.

(a) l l   (b) l l   (c) l l   (d) l l   (e) l l

60. The meter readings in an ac power circuit are 120 V RMS, 35 A RMS and a power factor of 0.75 lagging. The actual (true) power consumed is:
(a) 4200 W   (b) 42 kW   (c) 3150 W
(d) 31.5 kW   (e) 35 kW

(a) l l   (b) l l   (c) l l   (d) l l   (e) l l

61. Four conducting materials in the order of their conductivity are:
(a) gold, copper, silver, lead.
(b) silver, gold, copper, platinum.
(c) silver, copper, aluminum, zinc.
(d) silver, aluminum, gold, platinum.
(e) gold, copper, zinc, steel.

(a) l l   (b) l l   (c) l l   (d) l l   (e) l l

62. The frequency of a station in the Public Safety Radio Services that uses a crystal-controlled oscillator must be measured (according to the FCC rules and regulations) at least:
(a) once a year.
(b) when any change is made in the transmitter which may affect the carrier frequency.
(c) when the transmitter is first installed.
(d) when any change is made in the transmitter which may affect its frequency stability.
(e) All of the above are true.

(a) l l   (b) l l   (c) l l   (d) l l   (e) l l

63. The schematic shown in Fig. 6 is a two-stage audio amplifier used in a communications receiver. No signal appears in the loudspeaker. Which of the following is a possible cause?
(a) An open circuit in the filament of V2.
(b) S1 open.
(c) A short across R5.
(d) A short across R4.
(e) All the above are possible causes.

(a) l l   (b) l l   (c) l l   (d) l l   (e) l l

64. In the schematic of Fig. 6, C5 becomes open. Which of the following would occur?
(a) The audio output would be less but the fidelity would improve.
(b) There would be an increased bias on the output stage.
(c) Severe distortion would be heard in the audio output.
(d) Regenerative feedback would be applied to the output stage.
(e) None of the above would occur.

(a) l l   (b) l l   (c) l l   (d) l l   (e) l l

65. In the schematic of Fig. 6, the plate current of V2 is measured and found to be zero. Which of the following is a possible cause?
(a) R7 is an open circuit.
(b) C4 is a short circuit.

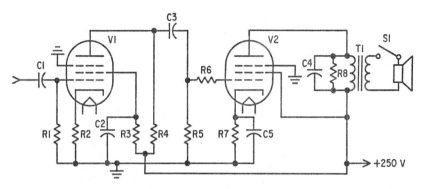

FIGURE 6

(c) R8 is an open circuit.
(d) There is a short circuit across R5.
(e) The primary of T1 is an open circuit.

(a) I I   (b) I I   (c) I I   (d) I I   (e) I I

66. In the schematic of Fig. 6, if R8 is an open circuit, which of the following would occur?
(a) Normal operation since R8 is used only to protect T1.
(b) The audio output signal in the loudspeaker would be distorted.
(c) The sound in the loudspeaker would vanish.
(d) An increase in the amount of treble.
(e) The plate current of V2 would increase sharply.

(a) I I   (b) I I   (c) I I   (d) I I   (e) I I

67. In the schematic of Fig. 6, if there is a short circuit across R5, which of the following would occur?
(a) There would be zero bias on the grid of V2 with respect to the cathode.
(b) An increase in the plate current of V2.
(c) Distortion in the loudspeaker would increase.
(d) No output signal in the loudspeaker.
(e) Both (a) and (b) are true.

(a) I I   (b) I I   (c) I I   (d) I I   (e) I I

68. In the schematic of Fig. 6, if C3 is shorted, which of the following would occur?
(a) The dc plate current of V2 would increase.
(b) A distorted signal output from the loudspeaker.
(c) The plate of V1 would become red-hot.
(d) The screen current of V2 would fall.
(e) Both (a) and (b) are true.

(a) I I   (b) I I   (c) I I   (d) I I   (e) I I

69. In the schematic of Fig. 6, the dc potential on the control grid of V2 is measured at zero volts to ground. Which of the following is a possible cause?
(a) This is true of normal operation.

(b) The filament of V2 is an open circuit.
(c) A short circuit between the control grid of V1 and ground.
(d) C5 is a short circuit.
(e) R7 is an open circuit.

(a) I I   (b) I I   (c) I I   (d) I I   (e) I I

70. In the schematic of Fig. 6, if C4 is an open circuit, which of the following results would occur? There would be:
(a) a normal signal output from the loudspeaker since C4 is only used to protect T1.
(b) an increase in the amount of treble in the loudspeaker.
(c) a decrease in the amount of bass.
(d) an increase in the screen current of V2.
(e) a decrease in the plate current of V2.

(a) I I   (b) I I   (c) I I   (d) I I   (e) I I

71. Which of the diagrams in Fig. 7 best represents the horizontal radiation pattern of a horizontal Hertz antenna?

(a) I I   (b) I I   (c) I I   (d) I I   (e) I I

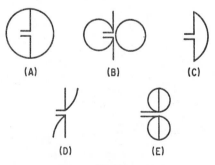

(A)   (B)   (C)

(D)   (E)

FIGURE 7

72. What is the approximate fully charged voltage of a lead acid cell?
(a) 1.75 V   (b) 2.06 V   (c) 2.5 V
(d) 6.3 V   (e) 12.6 V

(a) I I   (b) I I   (c) I I   (d) I I   (e) I I

73. An FM receiver whose IF is 10.7 MHz is experiencing image interference from a station operating on 118.4 MHz. Assuming that the incoming signal frequency is below that of the local oscillator, the receiver is tuned to:
(a) 97.0 MHz (b) 107.7 MHz
(c) 129.1 MHz (d) 139.8 MHz
(e) 102.35 MHz

(a) I I (b) I I (c) I I (d) I I (e) I I

74. The human ear can detect a minimum sound level change of:
(a) 1 B (b) 3 B (c) 1 W (d) 1 dB
(e) 3 dB

(a) I I (b) I I (c) I I (d) I I (e) I I

75. Which of the following statements about the use of a bleeder resistor in power supplies is false?
(a) Bleeder resistors may be either carbon or wirewound.
(b) If a bleeder resistor burns out, one of the filter capacitors is shorted.
(c) A bleeder resistor is desirable when using a choke input filter with no load.
(d) A bleeder resistor may be in the form of a voltage divider that will supply more than one output voltage.
(e) Bleeder resistors discharge the filter capacitors when the rectifier is switched off.

(a) I I (b) I I (c) I I (d) I I (e) I I

76. A coil of 10 mH has an inductive reactance of 49 ohms. If the source frequency is doubled, find the new inductive reactance.
(a) 38 ohms. (b) 98 ohms.
(c) 9.5 ohms. (d) 24.5 ohms.
(e) 196 ohms.

(a) I I (b) I I (c) I I (d) I I (e) I I

77. If the resistance in a dc circuit is doubled, the power dissipation may be kept the same by:
(a) doubling the voltage.
(b) halving the voltage.
(c) squaring the voltage.
(d) multiplying the voltage by 1.414.
(e) using four times the voltage.

(a) I I (b) I I (c) I I (d) I I (e) I I

78. "Thermistors" are used to:
(a) thermally insulate a crystal oven.
(b) increase the static base current during an increase in temperature.
(c) prevent "thermal runaway" in transistor circuits.
(d) reduce the reverse bias between the base and the emitter junction.
(e) reduce thermal noise in a transistor.

(a) I I (b) I I (c) I I (d) I I (e) I I

79. SHF (superhigh frequency) refers to the band of frequencies from:
(a) 3000 to 30,000 MHz
(b) 30,000 MHz to 300 GHz
(c) 3000 to 30,000 kHz
(d) 30,000 kHz to 3000 MHz
(e) None of the above are true.

(a) I I (b) I I (c) I I (d) I I (e) I I

80. If an HF carrier frequency is increased, the:
(a) skip distance increases.
(b) silent zone decreases.
(c) surface wave range increases.
(d) sky wave is returned by the D layer.
(e) depth to which the sky wave penetrates the ionosphere is reduced.

(a) I I (b) I I (c) I I (d) I I (e) I I

81. One method of decreasing harmonic radiation is by using:
(a) an electron-coupled oscillator.
(b) a low-reluctance screen.
(c) a grounded-grid stage.
(d) a Faraday screen.
(e) a cathode follower.

(a) I I (b) I I (c) I I (d) I I (e) I I

82. A quartz crystal may be placed in a thermostatically controlled oven in order to:
(a) improve the frequency stability.
(b) stop the crystal from vibrating violently.
(c) reduce excessive feedback.
(d) prevent excessive output from the oscillator.
(e) prevent the crystal from changing shape.

(a) I I (b) I I (c) I I (d) I I (e) I I

83. A specialized UHF tube is the:
(a) hexode. (b) heptode.
(c) pentagrid converter.
(d) lighthouse triode. (e) duo-diode triode.

(a) I I (b) I I (c) I I (d) I I (e) I I

84. What would be the result of shunting a resistor across a high Q parallel LC tank circuit at resonance?
(a) The Q would be increased.
(b) The bandwidth would increase.
(c) The resonant frequency would fall greatly.
(d) The impedance would rise.
(e) Both (a) and (d) are correct.

(a) I I (b) I I (c) I I (d) I I (e) I I

85. A simple crystal-controlled version of the Colpitts oscillator is the:
(a) Miller oscillator.
(b) TPTG oscillator.
(c) Pierce oscillator.
(d) Franklin oscillator.
(e) Armstrong oscillator.

(a) I I (b) I I (c) I I (d) I I (e) I I

86. Which of the following expressions represents the energy stored in a capacitor?
(a) $CE^2/2$ (b) CI^2
(c) Q^2/C (d) $QE^2/2$
(e) $E^2/2Q$

(a) | | (b) | | (c) | | (d) | | (e) | |

87. Operating during the period of an emergency:
(a) certain provisions of the station license need not be regarded.
(b) you may not transmit under any circumstances.
(c) you must call the FCC district office for permission to continue your programming.
(d) you may not operate with your regular programming.
(e) you are permitted to keep on programming but cannot use your own call letters. Use call letters that are confusing.

(a) | | (b) | | (c) | | (d) | | (e) | |

88. The plate of a rectifier tube suddenly becomes red-hot. One reason is a:
(a) shorted input capacitor.
(b) short between B+ and ground.
(c) short across the load.
(d) short between the filter choke and ground.
(e) All of the above are true.

(a) | | (b) | | (c) | | (d) | | (e) | |

89. An RF choke can be used:
(a) as part of the plate load of a shunt-fed RF amplifier.
(b) to provide grid-leak bias.
(c) to offer high resistance to audio currents but a virtual short to dc.
(d) to provide an inductance of several henries.
(e) Both (b) and (c) are true.

(a) | | (b) | | (c) | | (d) | | (e) | |

90. Quartz crystals should be cleaned with:
(a) TV tuner, cleaner-lubricator.
(b) paraffin.
(c) gasoline.
(d) carbon tetrachloride.
(e) Both (a) and (d) are true.

(a) | | (b) | | (c) | | (d) | | (e) | |

91. A beam power tube does not contain a:
(a) screen grid.   (b) control grid.
(c) cathode.   (d) suppressor grid.
(e) plate.

(a) | | (b) | | (c) | | (d) | | (e) | |

92. What is the total inductance between points A and B in Fig. 8?
(a) 3.33 mH   (b) 6.67 mH   (c) 60 mH
(d) 30 mH   (e) 5 mH

(a) | | (b) | | (c) | | (d) | | (e) | |

93. When neutralizing an RF power amplifier stage:

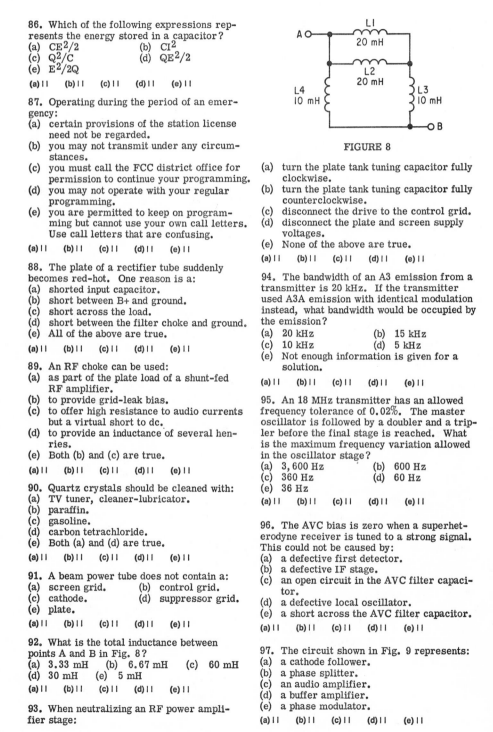

FIGURE 8

(a) turn the plate tank tuning capacitor fully clockwise.
(b) turn the plate tank tuning capacitor fully counterclockwise.
(c) disconnect the drive to the control grid.
(d) disconnect the plate and screen supply voltages.
(e) None of the above are true.

(a) | | (b) | | (c) | | (d) | | (e) | |

94. The bandwidth of an A3 emission from a transmitter is 20 kHz. If the transmitter used A3A emission with identical modulation instead, what bandwidth would be occupied by the emission?
(a) 20 kHz   (b) 15 kHz
(c) 10 kHz   (d) 5 kHz
(e) Not enough information is given for a solution.

(a) | | (b) | | (c) | | (d) | | (e) | |

95. An 18 MHz transmitter has an allowed frequency tolerance of 0.02%. The master oscillator is followed by a doubler and a tripler before the final stage is reached. What is the maximum frequency variation allowed in the oscillator stage?
(a) 3,600 Hz   (b) 600 Hz
(c) 360 Hz   (d) 60 Hz
(e) 36 Hz

(a) | | (b) | | (c) | | (d) | | (e) | |

96. The AVC bias is zero when a superheterodyne receiver is tuned to a strong signal. This could not be caused by:
(a) a defective first detector.
(b) a defective IF stage.
(c) an open circuit in the AVC filter capacitor.
(d) a defective local oscillator.
(e) a short across the AVC filter capacitor.

(a) | | (b) | | (c) | | (d) | | (e) | |

97. The circuit shown in Fig. 9 represents:
(a) a cathode follower.
(b) a phase splitter.
(c) an audio amplifier.
(d) a buffer amplifier.
(e) a phase modulator.

(a) | | (b) | | (c) | | (d) | | (e) | |

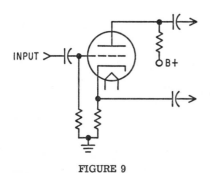

INPUT

B+

FIGURE 9

98. A vibrator is used to:
(a) change directly from a low dc voltage to a high dc voltage.
(b) rectify the ac in the primary circuit.
(c) reduce the possibility of RF appearing in the power supply.
(d) enable the dc battery voltage to drive an alternating current through a transformer primary.
(e) change from a high dc voltage to a low dc voltage with minimum power loss.

(a) ǀ ǀ   (b) ǀ ǀ   (c) ǀ ǀ   (d) ǀ ǀ   (e) ǀ ǀ

99. In an ac inductive circuit, the:
(a) voltage lags the current by 90°.
(b) voltage and the current are 180° out of phase.
(c) voltage and the current are in phase.
(d) current leads the voltage.
(e) apparent power is greater than the true power.

(a) ǀ ǀ   (b) ǀ ǀ   (c) ǀ ǀ   (d) ǀ ǀ   (e) ǀ ǀ

100. In the circuit shown in Fig. 10, what is the current through the 560 ohm resistor?
(a) 3750 μ A   (b) 4.25 mA
(c) 4.45 mA   (d) 4.85 mA
(e) 0.65 mA

(a) ǀ ǀ   (b) ǀ ǀ   (c) ǀ ǀ   (d) ǀ ǀ   (e) ǀ ǀ

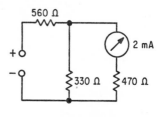

FIGURE 10

Element 3, Test 9

1. The inductance of an iron-core inductor is:
(a) directly proportional to the coil's length.
(b) inversely proportional to the cross-sectional area.
(c) inversely proportional to the permeability of the core.
(d) inversely proportional to the square of the number of turns.
(e) None of the above are true.

(a) || (b) || (c) || (d) || (e) ||

2. If a resistor is connected in parallel with a resonant tank circuit, the:
(a) Q of the circuit will increase.
(b) impedance at resonance will increase.
(c) impedance will remain unchanged.
(d) bandwidth will decrease.
(e) impedance will decrease.

(a) || (b) || (c) || (d) || (e) ||

3. A VR tube is used in the circuit of Fig. 1 to stabilize the load voltage at 150 V. What is the current through the VR tube?
(a) 2 mA   (b) 18 mA
(c) 25 mA   (d) 20 mA
(e) Less than 5 mA

(a) || (b) || (c) || (d) || (e) ||

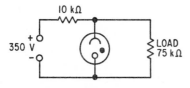

FIGURE 1

4. Comparing the properties of triodes and pentodes as audio voltage amplifiers:
(a) triodes have much higher ac plate resistances.
(b) pentodes can have much larger signal inputs.
(c) pentodes have higher gain.
(d) triodes have higher input impedances.

(e) pentodes have a lower level of third harmonic distortion.

(a) || (b) || (c) || (d) || (e) ||

5. If an FM signal is producing strong harmonics, how would its signal be heard on a receiver tuned to the second harmonic of the carrier frequency?
(a) The signal would be received but would be unintelligible.
(b) Only odd harmonics are radiated from an FM transmitter.
(c) The signal would be received and intelligible, but the frequency deviation would be doubled.
(d) The signal would be received and intelligible, but the modulation index would be halved.
(e) The signal would be received and intelligible, but the de-emphasis circuit would distort the audio output.

(a) || (b) || (c) || (d) || (e) ||

6. The commutator of a generator should never be cleaned with:
(a) fine sandpaper.
(b) nonconducting crocus cloth.
(c) emery paper.
(d) commutator paste.
(e) canvas.

(a) || (b) || (c) || (d) || (e) ||

7. The schematic shown in Fig. 2 is the driver/IPA assembly, used in an RCA mobile transmitter for use between 148 to 174 MHz. Terminal 106, +28 V input lead, has a resistor in series with it of 0.24 ohm for test purposes. How could the driver and IPA be tuned with a 50 ohm dummy load connected between the 50 ohm output and ground?
(a) First tune C13 and then C9 for a maximum drive to the following power amplifier.
(b) Measure the base-to-ground voltage of Q2 with an RF VTVM, and then tune C2, C9 and C13 for a maximum reading.

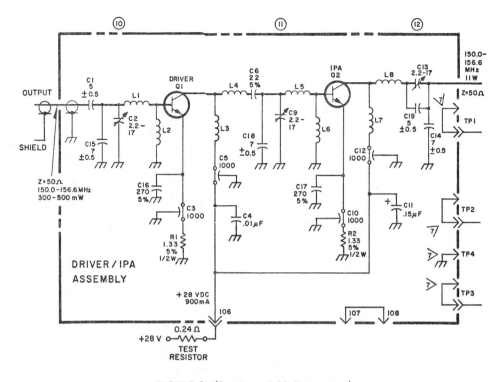

FIGURE 2   (Courtesy, RCA Corporation)

(c) Connect a dc voltmeter across the test
resistor, and tune C2, C9 and C13 for a
minimum reading.

(d) Follow (c) above, but tune for a maximum
reading.

(e) Place an RF voltmeter at the collector
of Q2, and tune C13 and C2 for a maximum reading, in that order.

(a) I I   (b) I I   (c) I I   (d) I I   (e) I I

8. In the schematic of Fig. 2, which of the
following statements is false?

(a) The dc voltage at the collector of Q2 is
approximately +28 V.

(b) The dc voltage at the collector of Q1 is
approximately +28 V.

(c) The dc voltage at the emitter of Q2 is
positive with respect to ground.

(d) The dc voltage at the emitter of Q1 is
less than the dc voltage at the emitter of
Q2.

(e) The dc voltage at the emitter of Q1 is
negative with respect to ground.

(a) I I   (b) I I   (c) I I   (d) I I   (e) I I

9. In the schematic of Fig. 2, there is no
output signal voltage appearing across C14.
The dc voltage across R2 is zero. What is a
possible cause?

(a) L7 is open.
(b) L8 is open.
(c) There is a short across R2.
(d) C1 is open.
(e) Both (a) and (b) are true.

(a) I I   (b) I I   (c) I I   (d) I I   (e) I I

10. In the schematic of Fig. 2, what class of
bias is used for Q1 and Q2?

(a) Class A.   (b) Class AB_1.
(c) Class AB_2.   (d) Class B.
(e) Class C.

(a) I I   (b) I I   (c) I I   (d) I I   (e) I I

11. In the schematic of Fig. 2, if there is no
input signal, which of the following statements
is true?

(a) The voltage across R2 is positive and
normal.

(b) The voltage across R1 is negative.

(c) The voltage across the test resistor is
zero.

(d) Excessive current is drawn by Q1 and
Q2, leading to thermal runaway and destruction of the transistor.

(e) The Q1 amplifier will self-oscillate.

(a) I I   (b) I I   (c) I I   (d) I I   (e) I I

12. An otherwise perfectly aligned FM transmitter has a doubler stage that is slightly detuned. When there is no modulation applied, the output carrier frequency is:
(a) seriously affected by carrier shift.
(b) not affected.
(c) increased.
(d) decreased.
(e) either increased or decreased depending on whether the doubler stage is tuned too high or too low.

(a) || (b) || (c) || (d) || (e) ||

13. In a Hartley oscillator, feedback is developed:
(a) across a capacitor.
(b) across a tapped resistor.
(c) across a tapped coil.
(d) through RC coupling.
(e) through interelectrode capacitance.

(a) || (b) || (c) || (d) || (e) ||

14. Which of the following would preferably be used for an RF doubler stage?
(a) A parallel arrangement.
(b) Neutralized triodes.
(c) Class B operation.
(d) A push-pull arrangement.
(e) A push-push arrangement.

(a) || (b) || (c) || (d) || (e) ||

15. What is the gain (voltage amplification factor) of a triode amplifier with a μ of 20, an ac plate resistance of 8 kohms, a load resistor of 22 kohms, a plate supply voltage of 250 V and a grid bias of -14 V?
(a) 20   (b) 18.6   (c) 14.7   (d) 12.3
(e) 10.2

(a) || (b) || (c) || (d) || (e) ||

16. If a device has a power loss of 30 dB, the ratio of output power to input power is:

(a) 1000 to 1   (b) 1 to 1000
(c) 30 to 1   (d) 1 to 30
(e) 1 to 300

(a) || (b) || (c) || (d) || (e) ||

17. The harmonic attenuation of a transmitter may be measured with:
(a) a VTVM.
(b) an absorption wavemeter.
(c) a wavetrap.
(d) a digital frequency meter.
(e) a field strength meter.

(a) || (b) || (c) || (d) || (e) ||

18. A motor-generator set that converts one value of dc voltage to another is called:
(a) a dynamo.   (b) a dynamotor.
(c) a vibrator.   (d) a dynamometer.
(e) an inverter.

(a) || (b) || (c) || (d) || (e) ||

19. A buffer RF amplifier is commonly used to:
(a) couple the final RF power amplifier to the antenna system.
(b) couple together two frequency multipliers.
(c) isolate the modulated stage from the modulator stage.
(d) couple the modulator to the RF output stage.
(e) isolate the oscillator from the following stage.

(a) || (b) || (c) || (d) || (e) ||

20. A swinging choke is normally found in:
(a) transmitter power supplies.
(b) antenna tuning systems.
(c) the grid circuit of RF amplifiers.
(d) receiver power supply circuits.
(e) grid bias supply circuits.

(a) || (b) || (c) || (d) || (e) ||

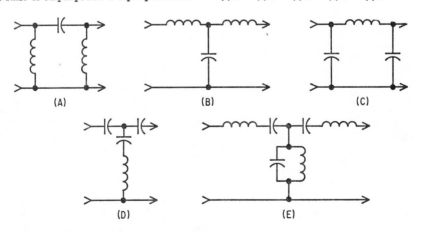

(A)   (B)   (C)

(D)   (E)

FIGURE 3

21. Which circuit in Fig. 3 is a high-pass filter?
(a) Circuit (a).
(b) Circuit (b).
(c) Circuit (c).
(d) Both circuits (d) and (e) are high-pass filters.
(e) Both circuits (a) and (d) are high-pass filters.

(a) I I   (b) I I   (c) I I   (d) I I   (e) I I

22. Which of the following is a relaxation oscillator?
(a) Multivibrator.   (b) Hartley.
(c) Colpitts.   (d) TPTG.
(e) Butler.

(a) I I   (b) I I   (c) I I   (d) I I   (e) I I

23. The meters in Fig. 4 read the values as recorded at an ac source. What is the true power consumption?
(a) 7.35 kW   (b) 10.5 kW
(c) 49 kW   (d) 1.05 kW
(e) 4.9 kW

(a) I I   (b) I I   (c) I I   (d) I I   (e) I I

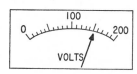

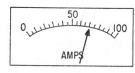

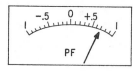

FIGURE 4

24. The stage at which the image channel must be rejected in a superheterodyne receiver is the:
(a) RF amplifier.   (b) IF amplifier.
(c) first detector.   (d) second detector.
(e) AF stage.

(a) I I   (b) I I   (c) I I   (d) I I   (e) I I

25. A transmitter has an authorized carrier frequency of 30 MHz. With no modulation the carrier frequency is measured at 30.0003 MHz. Which of the following is (are) a true statement(s)?
(a) If the tolerance is 0.0005%, it is an illegal transmission.

(b) The transmitter is out of tolerance by 0.001%.
(c) If the tolerance is 0.002%, it is a legal transmission.
(d) Only (b) and (c) are true.
(e) (a), (b) and (c) are true.

(a) I I   (b) I I   (c) I I   (d) I I   (e) I I

26. All new station license applications must:
(a) be notarized.
(b) be signed by the applicant.
(c) be prepared and signed by an approved consulting firm.
(d) be made in quadruplicate and signed and notarized by the consulting firm.
(e) Both (b) and (d) above are true.

(a) I I   (b) I I   (c) I I   (d) I I   (e) I I

27. A solenoid whose resistance is 400 ohms is connected in series with a resistor across a 120 V dc source. The circuit current is 0.2 A. How much power is dissipated in the resistor?
(a) 12 W   (b) 1.2 W   (c) Zero W
(d) 8 W   (e) 0.8 W

(a) I I   (b) I I   (c) I I   (d) I I   (e) I I

28. An advantage of an M-derived filter over a constant K-type is:
(a) that fewer components are used.
(b) that it is easier to design and therefore less costly.
(c) the sharper cut-off.
(d) the absence of resonant frequencies.
(e) the less sharp cut-off.

(a) I I   (b) I I   (c) I I   (d) I I   (e) I I

29. Transit-time effect in a triode can be reduced by:
(a) decreasing the spacing between the control grid and cathode.
(b) decreasing the spacing between the plate and cathode.
(c) reducing lead inductance.
(d) grounding the grid.
(e) A combination of (a) and (b) are true.

(a) I I   (b) I I   (c) I I   (d) I I   (e) I I

30. What is the circuit shown in Fig. 5?
(a) AF cathode follower with class A operation provided by cathode bias.
(b) AF voltage amplifier with a grounded cathode and class A operation.
(c) RF pentode voltage amplifier with cathode bias.
(d) AF pentode power amplifier with class A operation.
(e) AF beam power pentode amplifier with class B operation.

(a) I I   (b) I I   (c) I I   (d) I I   (e) I I

31. An end-fed quarter wave vertical antenna:
(a) requires a ground plane for effective operation.

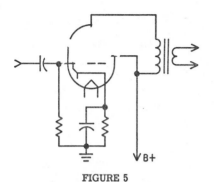

FIGURE 5

(b) radiates equally well in all vertical directions.
(c) radiates equally well in all horizontal directions.
(d) has an antenna resistance of 72 ohms at the feed point.
(e) Both (a) and (c) are true.

(a) I I   (b) I I   (c) I I   (d) I I   (e) I I

32. Which of the following is an important characteristic of a resonant cavity?
(a) It has a very high Q.
(b) It has a high overtone output when in oscillation.

(c) It is convenient to use in HF communications equipment.
(d) It has a very wide frequency response.
(e) The capacitance of the tuned circuit must use mica as a dielectric.

(a) I I   (b) I I   (c) I I   (d) I I   (e) I I

33. An audio amplifier uses a tube whose amplification factor is 20. This means that the:
(a) voltage gain is 20.
(b) current gain is 20.
(c) power gain is 20.
(d) current gain is greater than 20.
(e) voltage gain is less than 20.

(a) I I   (b) I I   (c) I I   (d) I I   (e) I I

34. The schematic shown in Fig. 6 is the PA assembly used in an RCA mobile transmitter for use between 148 to 174 MHz. TP1 through TP3 are test points. The input signal is applied to C1. Q1, Q2 and Q3 are in parallel to:
(a) improve the reliability of the amplifier should one of the transistors fail.
(b) provide approximately three times the power output of one transistor.
(c) decrease the input impedance of the amplifier.
(d) triple the operating frequency.
(e) None of the above are true.

(a) I I   (b) I I   (c) I I   (d) I I   (e) I I

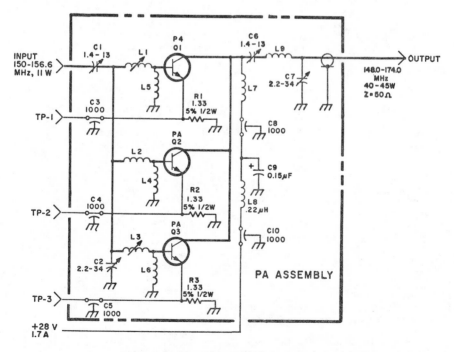

FIGURE 6   (Courtesy, RCA Corporation)

35. In the schematic of Fig. 6, the input signal is normal but there is no output. A possible cause for this failure is that:
(a) L8 is open.   (b) L1 is open.
(c) L5 is shorted.   (d) R1 is open.
(e) None of the above are true.

(a) | | (b) | | (c) | | (d) | | (e) | |

36. In the schematic of Fig. 6, the input signal is normal, but the output power, while not zero, is subnormal. A possible cause for this condition is that:
(a) L7 is open.   (b) C2 is shorted.
(c) R2 has a short across it.
(d) C9 is open.   (e) R1 is open.

(a) | | (b) | | (c) | | (d) | | (e) | |

37. In the schematic of Fig. 6, what class of bias is used for Q1, Q2 and Q3?
(a) Class A.   (b) Class AB_1.
(c) Class AB_2.   (d) Class B.
(e) Class C.

(a) | | (b) | | (c) | | (d) | | (e) | |

38. The circuit shown in Fig. 7 represents:
(a) cathode modulation.
(b) grid modulation.
(c) plate modulation.
(d) TPTG oscillator.
(e) reactance tube modulator.

(a) | | (b) | | (c) | | (d) | | (e) | |

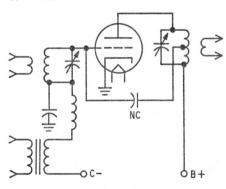

FIGURE 7

39. In the schematic of Fig. 6, L1 and L3 are adjustable to:
(a) match the amplifier input impedance.
(b) precisely set the frequency limits of the band-pass.
(c) insure that the three emitter currents are equal.
(d) neutralize the amplifier.
(e) None of the above are true.

(a) | | (b) | | (c) | | (d) | | (e) | |

40. In the Public Safety Radio Services, what is the maximum allowable frequency deviation for FM transmitters in the band from 470-512 MHz?
(a) 3 kHz   (b) 4 kHz   (c) 5 kHz
(d) 15 kHz   (e) 75 kHz

(a) | | (b) | | (c) | | (d) | | (e) | |

41. In the circuit shown in Fig. 8, what would an ac voltmeter read if connected between points A and B?
(a) 100 V   (b) 40 V   (c) 80 V
(d) 200 V   (e) 0 V

(a) | | (b) | | (c) | | (d) | | (e) | |

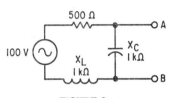

FIGURE 8

42. A high-gain tube suitable for an RF amplifier in a receiver would be a:
(a) low μ triode.   (b) beam power tube.
(c) tetrode.   (d) pentode.
(e) hexode.

(a) | | (b) | | (c) | | (d) | | (e) | |

43. The primary frequency standard is:
(a) WWV.   (b) WFCC.   (c) WNBS.
(d) operated by the FCC office in Washington, D.C.
(e) not available to unauthorized persons within the U.S.A.

(a) | | (b) | | (c) | | (d) | | (e) | |

44. In an FM transmitter, the amplitude of the audio signal is doubled and the modulating frequency is doubled. The frequency deviation (neglecting pre-emphasis) is:
(a) unchanged.   (b) doubled.
(c) multiplied by 4.   (d) halved.
(e) divided by 4.

(a) | | (b) | | (c) | | (d) | | (e) | |

45. The potential between points A and D in the circuit of Fig. 9 is 150 V. What is the potential between points D and B?
(a) +150 V   (b) +25 V   (c) +50 V
(d) 0 V   (e) -50 V

(a) | | (b) | | (c) | | (d) | | (e) | |

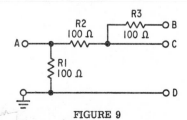

FIGURE 9

46. It is found that when the primary current in an audio transformer is increased, the flux density is not appreciably greater. This condition is known as:
(a) hysteresis.
(b) transformer distortion.
(c) eddy current peaking.
(d) core saturation.
(e) Normal condition.

(a) | | (b) | | (c) | | (d) | | (e) | |

47. The TPTG oscillator achieves positive feedback by using:
(a) inductive feedback from the coil of the tank circuit.
(b) the plate to control grid interelectrode capacitance.
(c) the screen grid to plate interelectrode capacitance.
(d) the plate to cathode interelectrode capacitance.
(e) the control grid to cathode interelectrode capacitance.

(a) | | (b) | | (c) | | (d) | | (e) | |

48. Class C amplifiers may be used as:
(a) pulse amplifiers.
(b) RF power amplifiers.
(c) clippers.
(d) harmonic amplifiers.
(e) All the above are true.

(a) | | (b) | | (c) | | (d) | | (e) | |

49. Placing an inductor in series with a quarter wavelength resonant antenna would:
(a) increase the RF current in the antenna.
(b) reduce the operating frequency of the antenna.
(c) not affect the antenna's resonant frequency.
(d) increase the operating frequency of the antenna.
(e) drastically change the radiation pattern of the antenna.

(a) | | (b) | | (c) | | (d) | | (e) | |

50. What is the peak value of a 10 V RMS sine wave?
(a) 28.28 V   (b) 14.14 V   (c) 7.07 V
(d) 10 V   (e) 6.36 V

(a) | | (b) | | (c) | | (d) | | (e) | |

51. A gaseous voltage regulator uses the following process for its operation:
(a) Electrodeposition.
(b) Electrode admittance.
(c) Electroluminescence.
(d) Ionization.
(e) Electrolysis.

(a) | | (b) | | (c) | | (d) | | (e) | |

52. The circuit shown in Fig. 10 represents:
(a) a blocking oscillator.
(b) a Hartley oscillator.

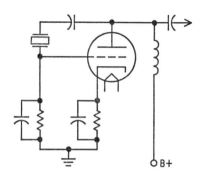

FIGURE 10

(c) a Pierce oscillator.
(d) an electron-coupled oscillator.
(e) a tuned-grid, tuned-plate oscillator.

(a) | | (b) | | (c) | | (d) | | (e) | |

53. The schematic shown in Fig. 11 is the frequency multiplier board used in an RCA mobile communications transmitter for operation in the 148 to 174 MHz range. If CR1 is shorted, which of the following is a true statement:
(a) The second doubler stage would be detuned.
(b) The output amplitude is greatly reduced.
(c) The DC voltage at TP-103 is zero.
(d) The signal voltage would appear at TP-103.
(e) None of the above is true.

(a) | | (b) | | (c) | | (d) | | (e) | |

54. In the schematic of Fig. 11, if R5 were open, which of the following statements would be false?
(a) The output signal is zero.
(b) The dc voltage at the collector of Q3 rises.
(c) The voltage at the base of Q3 falls.
(d) The dc current in the collector circuit of Q3 increases.
(e) The signal amplitude at the base of Q3 decreases.

(a) | | (b) | | (c) | | (d) | | (e) | |

55. In the schematic of Fig. 11, with a normal signal input, there is no output signal. TP-102 shows a negative dc voltage and TP-103 shows 0 dc voltage. Which of the following is a possible cause?
(a) There is a short across R5.
(b) C4 is shorted.
(c) L3 is open.
(d) C3 is shorted.
(e) There is a short across R8.

(a) | | (b) | | (c) | | (d) | | (e) | |

56. In the schematic of Fig. 11, the input to the multiplier board is 1 volt from the os-

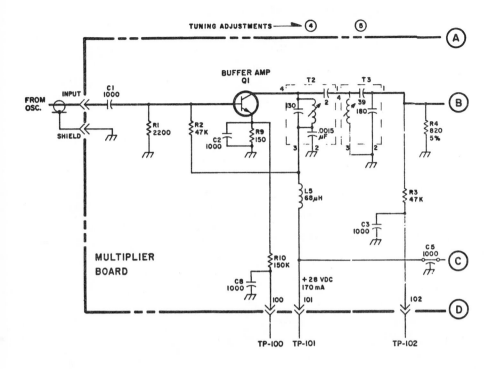

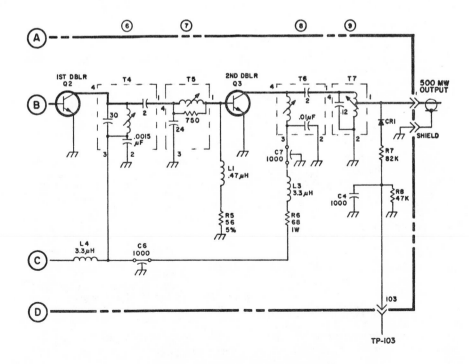

FIGURE 11 (Courtesy, RCA Corporation)

cillator. What is the probable class of operation of Q1, the RF amplifier?
(a) Class A.   (b) Class B.
(c) Class AB$_1$.   (d) Class AB$_2$.
(e) Class C.

(a) | | (b) | | (c) | | (d) | | (e) | |

57. In the schematic of Fig. 11, if there were no signal input to the circuit, which of the following statements would be false?
(a) No base-emitter current flows in Q2.
(b) The emitter of Q1 is at a positive potential.
(c) The dc collector to ground voltage is approximately +28 V.
(d) The second doubler, Q3, draws excessive collector current.
(e) Of the three transistors, only Q1 is conducting.

(a) | | (b) | | (c) | | (d) | | (e) | |

58. Advantages of crystal oscillators over variable frequency oscillators do not include:
(a) a higher degree of frequency stability.
(b) an extreme frequency stability if a thermostatically controlled oven is used to house the crystal.
(c) the requirement to switch crystals in order to cover various channels.
(d) an ability to be varied over a wide band of frequencies.
(e) Both (a) and (c) are true.

(a) | | (b) | | (c) | | (d) | | (e) | |

59. A coaxial cable with the outer conductor grounded:
(a) suffers from severe radiation loss.
(b) may be used for feeding some types of Marconi antenna directly.
(c) is a balanced feeder.
(d) may be used for feeding a Hertz diopole directly.
(e) is suitable for microwave frequencies above 10 GHz.

(a) | | (b) | | (c) | | (d) | | (e) | |

60. For Industrial Radio Services, the frequency of the transmitter must be checked directly or indirectly with (against):
(a) a grid dip meter.
(b) an absorption frequency meter.
(c) WWV.
(d) a frequency counter.
(e) an approved frequency meter.

(a) | | (b) | | (c) | | (d) | | (e) | |

61. Whether or not an element is a good conductor is governed by:
(a) its atomic structure.
(b) its valence structure.
(c) how many free electrons are available.
(d) All of the above are true.
(e) None of the above are true.

(a) | | (b) | | (c) | | (d) | | (e) | |

62. The true power consumed in an ac circuit depends on the:
(a) applied voltage.
(b) current drawn from the source.
(c) phase angle between the voltage and the current.
(d) power factor.
(e) All of the above are true.

(a) | | (b) | | (c) | | (d) | | (e) | |

63. An ohmmeter uses a 1.5 V battery and a moving coil meter movement with a sensitivity of 20,000 ohms per volt. What value of resistance is necessary to adjust the ohmmeter to zero (right side of the scale)?
(a) 20 kohms.   (b) 30 kohms.
(c) 50 kohms.   (d) 500 kohms.
(e) 5 Mohms.

(a) | | (b) | | (c) | | (d) | | (e) | |

64. It is not necessary to neutralize a grounded grid triode amplifier because the:
(a) stage has a low input impedance.
(b) input signal on the cathode and the output signal from the plate are in phase.
(c) gain of the stage is too low for self-oscillation to occur.
(d) grounded grid acts as a shield between the output plate circuit and the input cathode circuit.
(e) transit time effect is too great to allow self-oscillation.

(a) | | (b) | | (c) | | (d) | | (e) | |

65. The range of the space, or direct, wave depends on the:
(a) heights of the transmitting and receiving antennas.
(b) polarization of the radio wave.
(c) strength of the ionosphere.
(d) type of ground over which the radio wave travels.
(e) Both (b) and (d) are true.

(a) | | (b) | | (c) | | (d) | | (e) | |

66. A duly authorized person without pecuniary interest carrying on intercommunications for self-training and technical investigations is identified as:
(a) an amateur service.
(b) a citizens' radio service.
(c) a Public Safety Radio Service.
(d) a fixed station public service.
(e) a broadcast service.

(a) | | (b) | | (c) | | (d) | | (e) | |

67. A 25 circular mil wire has a resistance of 10 ohms per foot. Another 50 circular mil wire is made from the same material. How much resistance will 2 ft of the second wire have?
(a) 5 ohms.   (b) 10 ohms.
(c) 20 ohms.   (d) 40 ohms.

(e) 2.5 ohms.

(a) I I   (b) I I   (c) I I   (d) I I   (e) I I

68. The voltage and the current are 45° out of phase in a circuit containing:
(a) equal resistance and inductive reactance.
(b) equal resistance and capacitive reactance.
(c) inductive reactance but no resistance.
(d) capacitive reactance but no resistance.
(e) Both (a) and (b) are true.

(a) I I   (b) I I   (c) I I   (d) I I   (e) I I

69. Which type of instrument would give the most accurate dc voltage readings in high resistance circuits?
(a) VTVM.
(b) VOM.
(c) volt-amp-hour meter.
(d) gold leaf electroscope.
(e) galvanometer.

(a) I I   (b) I I   (c) I I   (d) I I   (e) I I

70. A triode grounded cathode RF amplifier must be neutralized:
(a) to prevent the stage from self-oscilla-ting.
(b) to prevent positive feedback.
(c) to prevent instability in the amplifier.
(d) unless the stage is a frequency multi-plier.
(e) All of the above are true.

(a) I I   (b) I I   (c) I I   (d) I I   (e) I I

71. What is the dc ohmic resistance of a quarter-wave Marconi antenna?
(a) 35 ohms.   (b) 70 ohms.
(c) 300 ohms.   (d) 800 ohms.
(e) Virtually zero.

(a) I I   (b) I I   (c) I I   (d) I I   (e) I I

72. F3 type emission is frequency (or phase) modulation:
(a) telegraphy by frequency shift keying without the use of a modulating audio frequency--one of two frequencies being emitted at any instant.
(b) telegraphy by the on-off keying of a fre-quency modulating audio frequency or by the on-off keying of a frequency modu-lated emission.
(c) telephony.
(d) facsimile by direct frequency modulation of the carrier.
(e) television.

(a) I I   (b) I I   (c) I I   (d) I I   (e) I I

73. When the current in the primary of a power transformer is 1.5 A, and the current in one half of the center-tapped secondary is 4.5 A, what is the primary to secondary turns ratio?
(a) 6 to 1   (b) 3 to 1

(c) 1 to 9   (d) 9 to 1
(e) 1 to 3

(a) I I   (b) I I   (c) I I   (d) I I   (e) I I

74. With 200 V on the plate of a triode, the cut-off bias value is -25 V. If the grid vol-tage is varied from -30 to -40 V, the:
(a) plate current remains zero.
(b) plate current increases.
(c) plate current decreases.
(d) cathode current increases.
(e) tube might be damaged.

(a) I I   (b) I I   (c) I I   (d) I I   (e) I I

75. In a class A audio pentode voltage ampli-fier, the cathode bias resistor carries the following currents:
(a) plate current only.
(b) screen current only.
(c) plate current and screen current.
(d) plate current, screen current and con-trol grid current.
(e) plate current, screen current and sup-pressor grid current.

(a) I I   (b) I I   (c) I I   (d) I I   (e) I I

76. Waveguides are used only at microwave frequencies because at lower frequencies:
(a) skin effect causes excessive losses in them.
(b) they would have to be too large.
(c) they cannot be curved.
(d) The statement is incorrect, since they are used at much lower frequencies.
(e) they would have to be too small to manu-facture.

(a) I I   (b) I I   (c) I I   (d) I I   (e) I I

77. What does the waveform shown in Fig. 12 represent?
(a) The voltage distribution on a quarter-wave Hertz antenna.
(b) The current distribution on a half-wave Hertz antenna.
(c) The current distribution on a quarter-wave Hertz antenna.
(d) The voltage distribution on a half-wave Hertz antenna.
(e) The voltage distribution on a quarter-wave Marconi antenna.

(a) I I   (b) I I   (c) I I   (d) I I   (e) I I

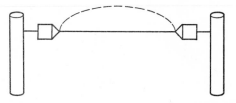

FIGURE 12

78. The power measured in a dc circuit is 320 W. In 15 hours, the energy used or work done is:
(a) 48 kW   (b) 4.8 kWh   (c) 480 W-hr
(d) 48 million joules   (e) 48 million ergs

(a) I I   (b) I I   (c) I I   (d) I I   (e) I I

79. How must the circuit shown in Fig. 13 be changed in order to operate correctly?
(a) Reverse D1.   (b) Reverse D2.
(c) Reverse D3.   (d) Reverse D4.
(e) Reverse D2 and D3.

(a) I I   (b) I I   (c) I I   (d) I I   (e) I I

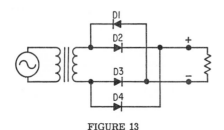

FIGURE 13

80. High power RF amplifier output stages are operated in class C:
(a) to minimize distortion.
(b) for high plate efficiency.
(c) to provide low level modulation.
(d) to reduce the production of harmonics.
(e) to reduce the level of input signal required to drive the stage.

(a) I I   (b) I I   (c) I I   (d) I I   (e) I I

81. In the circuit shown in Fig. 14, what must be added for correct operation of the circuit for class A operation?
(a) Nothing need be added.
(b) A neutralization circuit.
(c) A grid leak bias circuit.
(d) A cathode bias circuit.
(e) A by-pass capacitor between the grid and ground.

(a) I I   (b) I I   (c) I I   (d) I I   (e) I I

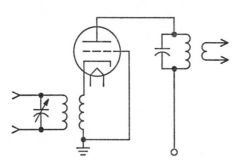

FIGURE 14

82. The schematic shown in Fig. 15 is an RCA Power Supply Board used in a mobile communications transmitter for use in the 148 to 174 MHz range. There is no dc output when the power supply is turned on. Which of the following could account for this?
(a) R11 is open.   (b) R12 is open.
(c) R13 has a short across it.
(d) R20 is open.   (e) R10 is open.

(a) I I   (b) I I   (c) I I   (d) I I   (e) I I

83. In the schematic of Fig. 15, the circuit of CR5 and CR6 is commonly known as a:
(a) half-wave rectifier.
(b) voltage doubler.
(c) bridge rectifier.
(d) full-wave rectifier.
(e) voltage converter.

(a) I I   (b) I I   (c) I I   (d) I I   (e) I I

84. In the schematic of Fig. 15, the adjusting resistor R17 has no effect on the output voltage. A possible cause is:
(a) R19 has a short across it.
(b) C14 is open.
(c) CR7 is open.
(d) L2 has a short across it.
(e) None of the above are true.

(a) I I   (b) I I   (c) I I   (d) I I   (e) I I

85. In the schematic of Fig. 15, the output voltage at terminal 101 is increased by:
(a) increasing the resistance of R3.
(b) decreasing the resistance of R10.
(c) increasing the resistance of R17.
(d) decreasing the resistance of R17.
(e) None of the above are true.

(a) I I   (b) I I   (c) I I   (d) I I   (e) I I

86. In the schematic of Fig. 15, the power supply remains on whether or not there is a voltage at terminal 3. What is a possible cause?
(a) R8 is open.   (b) R9 is open.
(c) R10 is shorted.
(d) Collector to emitter short of Q5.
(e) R20 is open.

(a) I I   (b) I I   (c) I I   (d) I I   (e) I I

87. In the schematic of Fig. 15, the circuit of Q1, Q2, Q3, and T1 function as a:
(a) push-pull amplifier.
(b) push-push amplifier.
(c) free-running multivibrator.
(d) shunt regulator.
(e) series regulator.

(a) I I   (b) I I   (c) I I   (d) I I   (e) I I

88. In the schematic of Fig. 15, the frequency of the signal at the collector of Q2 and Q3 is determined by the:
(a) inductance of T1's secondary winding and capacitor C9.
(b) saturation of the core of T1.

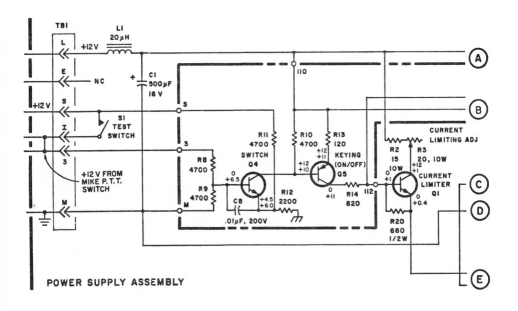

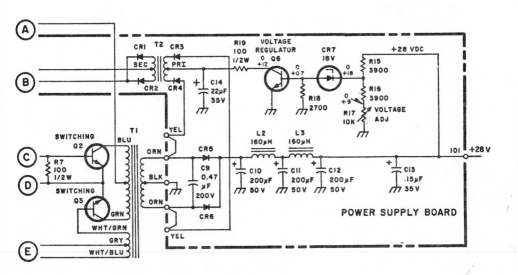

FIGURE 15   (Courtesy, RCA Corporation)

(c) value of R7.
(d) adjustment of R3.
(e) Zener voltage across CR9.

(a) I I   (b) I I   (c) I I   (d) I I   (e) I I

89. In the schematic of Fig. 15, the voltage wave form at the collector of Q2 is a:
(a) square wave.   (b) sine wave.
(c) half-wave rectified sine wave.
(d) series of narrow negative pulses.
(e) triangular wave.

(a) I I   (b) I I   (c) I I   (d) I I   (e) I I

90. The capacitor input filter, as compared with a similar choke input filter, has:
(a) more ripple in the output.
(b) better regulation.
(c) a lower dc output voltage.
(d) higher rectifier peak surge currents.
(e) None of the above are true.

(a) I I   (b) I I   (c) I I   (d) I I   (e) I I

91. The SHF range extends from:
(a) 3000 to 30,000 kHz
(b) 300 to 3000 kHz   (c) 30 to 300 kHz
(d) 3 to 30 GHz   (e) 30 to 300 GHz

(a) I I   (b) I I   (c) I I   (d) I I   (e) I I

92. To repair etched wiring printed-circuit boards, you require a:
(a) high melting point solder and a low wattage pencil type soldering iron.
(b) low melting point solder and a low wattage soldering iron.
(c) low melting point solder and a high wattage soldering gun.
(d) high melting point solder and a high wattage soldering gun.
(e) None of the above are true.

(a) I I   (b) I I   (c) I I   (d) I I   (e) I I

93. If a capacitive reactance of 1500 ohms is connected in series with a 1.5 kohm resistor, the phase angle is:
(a) 0° (b) $+90^o$ (c) -90° (d) $+45^o$
(e) -45°

(a) I I   (b) I I   (c) I I   (d) I I   (e) I I

94. A unit that is used to convert low voltage dc to a high voltage dc is a:
(a) dynometer.   (b) rectifier.
(c) inverter.   (d) dynamometer.
(e) vibrator power supply.

(a) I I   (b) I I   (c) I I   (d) I I   (e) I I

95. Core saturation of an audio stage's output transformer may be caused by:
(a) too low a value of B+ voltage.
(b) too large a value of grid bias voltage.
(c) too high a level of plate current through the primary.
(d) a weak signal applied to the primary.

(e) push-pull operation.

(a) I I   (b) I I   (c) I I   (d) I I   (e) I I

96. The function of a squelch circuit is:
(a) to prevent blasting of the loudspeaker.
(b) to reduce receiver sensitivity for all incoming signals.
(c) to prevent noise from reaching the loudspeaker when there is no incoming signal.
(d) the same as that of a noise limiter stage.
(e) to prevent AVC bias from fluctuating.

(a) I I   (b) I I   (c) I I   (d) I I   (e) I I

97. When a lead-acid storage cell is rapidly discharged and the plates become sulphated, the sulphation does not cause:
(a) an increase in the cell's amp-hour capacity.
(b) excessive internal I^2R losses.
(c) excessive heating of the cell.
(d) buckling of the plates in the cell.
(e) a lower output voltage from the cell.

(a) I I   (b) I I   (c) I I   (d) I I   (e) I I

98. Properties of a half-wave rectifier circuit include which of the following?
(a) Its ripple frequency is half that of a full-wave rectifier.
(b) It can be operated without a power transformer.
(c) Compared with a full-wave rectifier, it provides a higher dc output voltage for a given total secondary winding voltage.
(d) It reduces transformer insulation problems when providing high voltage outputs.
(e) All of the above are true.

(a) I I   (b) I I   (c) I I   (d) I I   (e) I I

99. A dipole antenna can be matched to a balanced transmission line by:
(a) a quarter-wave stub.
(b) a series connected, quarter-wave section whose surge impedance equals $\sqrt{Z_o}$ of the line x Z of the antenna.
(c) using a line whose surge impedance is equal to the antenna impedance.
(d) "Y-feeding" the dipole so that the surge impedance of the line equals the antenna impedance at the points the line meets the antenna.
(e) All the above are true.

(a) I I   (b) I I   (c) I I   (d) I I   (e) I I

100. Pre-emphasis is used in FM communications to improve the signal-to-noise ratio of:
(a) all modulating frequencies.
(b) low modulating frequencies.
(c) high modulating frequencies.
(d) the total significant sidebands.
(e) the total modulated carrier.

(a) I I   (b) I I   (c) I I   (d) I I   (e) I I

Element 8, Test 1

1. If the magnetron's magnet becomes too weak:
(a) there will be a high dc level of magnetron current.
(b) there will be a low dc level of magnetron current.
(c) the electron path will become more curved.
(d) the RF output from the magnetron will rise to a dangerously high level.
(e) Both (c) and (d) are true.

(a) I I   (b) I I   (c) I I   (d) I I   (e) I I

2. If the maximum target range of a radar set is to be doubled, the peak power output of the transmitter (assuming all other parameters are kept constant) must be multiplied by a factor of:
(a) 2   (b) 4   (c) 8   (d) 16   (e) 32

(a) I I   (b) I I   (c) I I   (d) I I   (e) I I

3. The maximum effective range of pulse radar equipment may be increased by:
(a) reducing the beam width for a given peak power output.
(b) increasing the transmitter's peak power output.
(c) increasing the receiver's signal-to-noise ratio at the input to the receiver by improving the design of the first mixer stage.
(d) increasing the pulse width within practical limits.
(e) All the above are true.

(a) I I   (b) I I   (c) I I   (d) I I   (e) I I

4. Which of the following stages of a pulse radar set may use the circuit shown in Fig. 1?
(a) Compensated video amplifier.
(b) IF amplifier.
(c) Pulse-amplifying circuit.
(d) Pulse limiter.
(e) AFC discriminator.

(a) I I   (b) I I   (c) I I   (d) I I   (e) I I

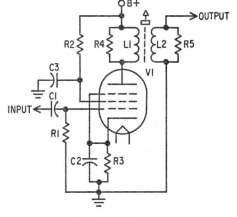

FIGURE 1

5. Measurements using a directional coupler indicate that the RF power reflected from the antenna is 4% of the incident power. What is the VSWR in the waveguide?
(a) 1.08 to 1   (b) 1.25 to 1
(c) 0.8 to 1   (d) 1.5 to 1
(e) 1.37 to 1

(a) I I   (b) I I   (c) I I   (d) I I   (e) I I

6. The circuit shown in Fig. 2 represents a radar:
(a) VHF oscillator.
(b) complete timer unit.
(c) blocking oscillator.
(d) modulator unit.
(e) synchronizer unit.

(a) I I   (b) I I   (c) I I   (d) I I   (e) I I

7. The purpose of a horn radiator is:
(a) to act as an impedance matching device between the waveguide and parabolic reflector and free space.
(b) to narrow the transmitted beam.
(c) to concentrate the electromagnetic energy into a narrow beam.

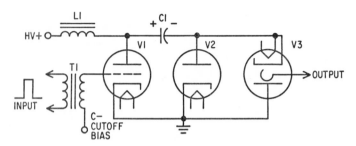

FIGURE 2

(d) to help in keeping moisture from entering the waveguide.
(e) Both (a) and (b) are true.

(a) I I   (b) I I   (c) I I   (d) I I   (e) I I

8. The common number of RF stages used in the superheterodyne receiver of a marine radar set is:
(a) 1   (b) 2   (c) 3   (d) 4   (e) None.

(a) I I   (b) I I   (c) I I   (d) I I   (e) I I

9. In merchant marine service, it is important to check for radar interference. Which of the following frequencies would not be of great interest?
(a) 100 to 200 kHz   (b) 350 to 515 kHz
(c) 1.85 to 1.950 MHz
(d) 2.0 to 30.0 MHz   (e) 54.0 to 60 MHz

(a) I I   (b) I I   (c) I I   (d) I I   (e) I I

10. If there is a 61.8 μ sec time interval between a radar pulse being transmitted and its target echo being received, what is the range of the target?
(a) 0.5 nautical miles.   (b) 5,000 yards.
(c) 5 nautical miles.
(d) 1.0 nautical miles.   (e) 25,000 yards.

(a) I I   (b) I I   (c) I I   (d) I I   (e) I I

11. Interference to the radio direction finding receiver caused by radar signals would be recognized by:
(a) a tone or "hash" that would appear in the receiver's output.
(b) an error in the direction finder's bearing.
(c) the inability to null the received signal.
(d) noise in the receiver output similar to atmospheric static.
(e) None of the above are true.

(a) I I   (b) I I   (c) I I   (d) I I   (e) I I

12. The artificial transmission line may be used:
(a) as a delay in the feeding of the various elements of the radar antenna array.
(b) as an alternative to the echo box.
(c) to determine the pulse width of the radar set.
(d) in the STC system.

(e) as part of the duplexer.

(a) I I   (b) I I   (c) I I   (d) I I   (e) I I

13. Which of the waveforms shown in Fig. 3 best represents the pulse shape and polarity applied to the magnetron?

(a) I I   (b) I I   (c) I I   (d) I I   (e) I I

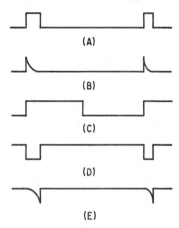

(A)

(B)

(C)

(D)

(E)

FIGURE 3

14. The mixer stage in an SHF radar receiver commonly uses a:
(a) transistorized detector.
(b) thermionic diode detector.
(c) silicon crystal diode.
(d) P-N junction diode.
(e) triode detector.

(a) I I   (b) I I   (c) I I   (d) I I   (e) I I

15. Interference to nearby radio communication receivers is sometimes caused by radar transmitters. The interference may be characterized by a steady AF tone. This is caused by:
(a) heterodyning between the local oscillator's fundamental frequency and the radar's carrier frequency.
(b) the pulse repetition rate of the radar keying system.

(c) the radar's carrier frequency being a harmonic of the receiver's intermediate frequency.
(d) the receiver being tuned to an upper sideband, contained in the radar's signal.
(e) an incorrect alignment of the filters included in the IF stages of the receiver.

(a) | | (b) | | (c) | | (d) | | (e) | |

16. Which of the following frequency bands has been allocated to ship radar transmitters?
(a) 2900 to 3100 MHz   (b) 6460 to 6650 MHz
(c) 3900 to 4100 MHz   (d) 8300 to 8500 MHz
(e) 10,300 to 10,500 MHz

(a) | | (b) | | (c) | | (d) | | (e) | |

17. Magnetrons are generally used in the frequency range of:
(a) 600 kHz to 3 GHz   (b) 3 GHz to 300 GHz
(c) 600 MHz to 30 GHz
(d) 60 MHz to 60 GHz
(e) 300 MHz to 30 GHz

(a) | | (b) | | (c) | | (d) | | (e) | |

18. For a pulse radar set operating near 3 GHz, a typical frequency for the receiver's IF would be:
(a) 30 MHz   (b) 10.7 MHz
(c) 455 kHz   (d) 1 MHz   (e) 5 MHz

(a) | | (b) | | (c) | | (d) | | (e) | |

19. Radar interference in communications receivers may be eliminated by:
(a) a wave trap.
(b) an RF noise clipper.
(c) using narrow band filters in the IF stages.
(d) a differential squelch circuit.
(e) None of the above are true.

(a) | | (b) | | (c) | | (d) | | (e) | |

20. Regarding a pulse radar set, which of the following is a true statement?
(a) The duty cycle is equal to the product of the pulse repetition time and the pulse frequency.
(b) The peak power is equal to the average power divided by the duty cycle.
(c) The ratio of the average power to the peak power is equal to the reciprocal of the duty cycle.
(d) Pulse duration = peak power/(average power x pulse frequency)
(e) Average power/pulse duration = peak power/duty cycle

(a) | | (b) | | (c) | | (d) | | (e) | |

21. If the duration of a radar pulse is $1\,\mu$ sec, what is the theoretical minimum range difference between two targets which cannot be separated on the display?
(a) 82 yd   (b) 164 yd
(c) 328 yd   (d) 656 yd
(e) 49.2 yd

(a) | | (b) | | (c) | | (d) | | (e) | |

22. The duplexer in a radar system is used to:
(a) prevent frequency "pulling" between the magnetron and the reflex klystron circuit.
(b) isolate the receiver from the transmitted pulse.
(c) prevent the magnetron from attenuating the target echo.
(d) isolate the receiver from the target echo.
(e) Both (b) and (c) are true.

(a) | | (b) | | (c) | | (d) | | (e) | |

23. A coaxial cable is used to transfer the echo pulse from the receiver to the PPI display. The output stage of the receiver is:
(a) a high gain video amplifier.
(b) a diode second detector.
(c) a pulse amplifier with a matching transformer that is resonant at the pulse repetition rate.
(d) an emitter (or cathode) follower.
(e) a pulse shaping circuit.

(a) | | (b) | | (c) | | (d) | | (e) | |

24. The "Heading Flash" that is used on radar sets is produced by:
(a) a synchronizing signal from the PPI sweep oscillator.
(b) an RC timing circuit that controls the PPI sweep oscillator circuit.
(c) a mechanical switch used in conjunction with the rotating antenna.
(d) the keyer circuit.
(e) the magnetron tube.

(a) | | (b) | | (c) | | (d) | | (e) | |

25. An aquadag coating in the CRT of a radar set may be used as:
(a) an anode.   (b) an electrostatic shield.
(c) a focusing screen.
(d) a magnetic shield.
(e) Both (a) and (b) are true.

(a) | | (b) | | (c) | | (d) | | (e) | |

26. The schematic shown in Fig. 4 represents:
(a) the input circuitry to an SHF pre-amplifier with overload protection provided by the diode.
(b) a directional coupler for determining the reflected power.
(c) the mixer stage of a radar receiver.
(d) part of a duplexer.
(e) part of an AFC system.

(a) | | (b) | | (c) | | (d) | | (e) | |

27. It is desired to produce range marker circles on a PPI display, with a separation of 1/2 nautical mile in range between adjacent circles. The frequency of the range marker oscillator would be:
(a) 186.2 kHz   (b) 161.7 kHz
(c) 93.1 kHz   (d) 323.4 kHz

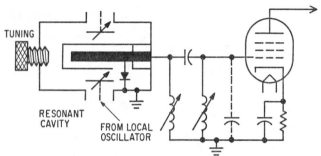

TUNING

RESONANT CAVITY

FROM LOCAL OSCILLATOR

FIGURE 4

(e) 213.8 kHz

(a) | | (b) | | (c) | | (d) | | (e) | |

28. The wide bandwidth required by the IF stages of a pulse radar receiver may be achieved by:
(a) R-C coupling between stages.
(b) damping resistors across the tuned circuits.
(c) double-tuned circuits with the degree of coupling greater than the critical value.
(d) "stagger" tuning.
(e) (b), (c) and (d) are true.

(a) | | (b) | | (c) | | (d) | | (e) | |

29. In a radar transmitter the pulse width is 1 μ sec, the pulse repetition time is 2000 μ sec, and the average power output is 50 W. What is the peak power output?
(a) 100 kW   (b) 50 kW   (c) 20 kW
(d) 10 kW   (e) 5 kW

(a) | | (b) | | (c) | | (d) | | (e) | |

30. The reflex klystron of a radar set is operating below the magnetron's frequency, which is drifting upwards. As a result the:
(a) IF frequency drift will equal the magnetron frequency drift.
(b) Klystron's frequency will drift downward.
(c) action of the AFC circuit will return the magnetron's frequency to its correct value.
(d) output from the AFC discriminator will make the klystron's repeller more negative.
(e) output from the AFC discriminator will make the klystron's repeller less negative.

(a) | | (b) | | (c) | | (d) | | (e) | |

31. The function of a reflex klystron in a radar set is the same as that of:
(a) an SHF voltage amplifier.
(b) a local oscillator.
(c) a pulse generator.
(d) a high power microwave amplifier.

(e) a high power transmitter-oscillator.

(a) | | (b) | | (c) | | (d) | | (e) | |

32. Which of the following statements regarding the entries made in the installation and maintenance records of a ship radar station is true?
(a) Entries shall be made by or under the personal supervision of the responsible installation, service, or maintenance operator concerned in each case.
(b) The station licensee is also jointly responsible for the faithful and accurate making of such entries.
(c) All entries shall be made by the ship's Master.
(d) Entries shall be made only by the Radio Officer.
(e) Both (a) and (b) are true.

(a) | | (b) | | (c) | | (d) | | (e) | |

33. Which of the following frequency bands has been allocated to ship radar transmitters?
(a) 1900 to 2100 MHz
(b) 2460 to 2650 MHz
(c) 5900 to 5100 MHz
(d) 5300 to 5500 MHz
(e) 9300 to 9500 MHz

(a) | | (b) | | (c) | | (d) | | (e) | |

34. In a marine radar set, the peak power output of a 0.2 μ sec pulse is 250 kW. If the pulse frequency is 500 Hz, what is the value of the duty cycle?
(a) 0.0001   (b) 0.0002
(c) 0.00025   (d) 0.0005
(e) 0.002

(a) | | (b) | | (c) | | (d) | | (e) | |

35. An operator who is responsible for the installation, servicing and maintenance of ship radar equipment must have obtained what class of FCC license?
(a) A First Class Radio Telephone or Radio Telegraph License with radar endorsement.

(b) A Second Class Radio Telephone or Radio
     Telegraph License with radar endorse-
     ment.
(c) A third Class Radio Telephone or Radio
     Telephone License with radar endorse-
     ment.
(d) A Second Class Radio Telegraph License
     with element nine endorsement.
(e) Both (a) and (b) are true.

(a) I I   (b) I I   (c) I I   (d) I I   (e) I I

36. In a radar set the peak power output is
200 kW, the pulse repetition rate is 500 Hz,
the pulse width is 0.7 μ sec. What is the
value of the duty cycle?
(a) 0.00070   (b) 0.00035
(c) 0.00014   (d) 0.00028
(e) 0.007

(a) I I   (b) I !   (c) I I   (d) I I   (e) I I

37. The sensitivity time control in a radar
set is used to:
(a) vary the pulse width for target discrimin-
     ation purposes.
(b) reduce the interference effect of the
     "sea return."
(c) provide a delayed automatic gain control
     for the echoes from distant targets.
(d) reduce the receiver gain for nearby
     targets.
(e) Both (b) and (d) are true.

(a) I I   (b) I I   (c) I I   (d) I I   (e) I I

38. The interior dimensions of a rectangular
waveguide are 1 1/2 by 4 cm. The cut-off
wavelength for the $TE_{1,0}$ mode is:
(a) 3 cm   (b) 4 cm   (c) 2 cm
(d) 0.75 cm   (e) 8 cm

(a) I I   (b) I I   (c) I I   (d) I I   (e) I I

39. Which of the voltage waveforms in Fig. 5
is applied to the deflection coils of a PPI tube?

(a) I I   (b) I I   (c) I I   (d) I I   (e) I I

40. The PPI display stands for:
(a) plan position indicator.
(b) plan pulse indicator.
(c) pulse position indicator.
(d) picture position indicator.
(e) picture plan indicator.

(a) I I   (b) I I   (c) I I   (d) I I   (e) I I

41. The echo box in a radar set is used:
(a) as a low Q resonant cavity for measuring
     the receiver's bandwidth.
(b) as a preamplifier for the received tar-
     get echoes.
(c) as a dummy antenna that can be matched
     to the magnetron.
(d) to provide an artificial target for test
     purposes.
(e) as part of the AFC system.

(a) I I   (b) I I   (c) I I   (d) I I   (e) I I

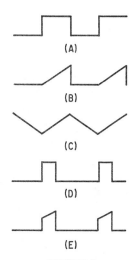

(A)

(B)

(C)

(D)

(E)

FIGURE 5

42. The second detector stage in a radar
receiver may use a:
(a) bipolar transistor.
(b) ratio detector circuit.
(c) thermionic diode.
(d) heterodyne mixer circuit.
(e) Foster Seeley discriminator.

(a) I I   (b) I I   (c) I I   (d) I I   (e) I I

43. In which of the following is a "keep-
alive" electrode always found?
(a) TR box tube.   (b) Magnetron.
(c) Reflex klystron.
(d) Anti-TR box tube.
(e) Thyratron in a modulator unit.

(a) I I   (b) I I   (c) I I   (d) I I   (e) I I

44. A pulse radar set with a peak power output of 1 MW, has a pulse repetition time of
2000 μ sec. What is the value of the pulse
frequency (repetition rate)?
(a) 100   (b) 150   (c) 200   (d) 400
(e) 500

(a) I I   (b) I I   (c) I I   (d) I I   (e) I I

45. If, in question 44, the average power output is 250 W, what is the value of the pulse
width (duration) in microseconds?
(a) 0.1   (b) 0.2   (c) 0.25   (d) 0.5
(e) 1.0

(a) I I   (b) I I   (c) I I   (d) I I   (e) I I

46. Choke joints are normally used to:
(a) provide a connection between two sec-
     tions of waveguide with very little loss
     of energy.
(b) provide electrical isolation between two
     sections of the waveguide system.
(c) allow the removal of parts of the wave-
     guide for repair or replacement.

(d) prevent vibrations in the antenna system from being transmitted to the magnetron.
(e) All the above are true.

(a) I I   (b) I I   (c) I I   (d) I I   (e) I I

47. The anode of a magnetron is usually:
(a) maintained at a high positive dc potential relative to ground.
(b) maintained at a high negative dc potential relative to ground.
(c) insulated from the chassis.
(d) made of high permeability material to provide a low reluctance path for the flux lines from the magnet.
(e) grounded.

(a) I I   (b) I I   (c) I I   (d) I I   (e) I I

48. With respect to the parabolic reflector, the waveguide horn is placed at the:
(a) apex of the reflector.
(b) vertex of the reflector.
(c) center of the reflector.
(d) focal point of the reflector.

(e) mid-point between the center and the vertex of the reflector.

(a) I I   (b) I I   (c) I I   (d) I I   (e) I I

49. A silicon crystal diode may be damaged by:
(a) excessive mechanical pressure.
(b) the use of excessively high frequencies.
(c) excessive electrostatic charges.
(d) excessive magnetic fields.
(e) Both (a) and (c) are true.

(a) I I   (b) I I   (c) I I   (d) I I   (e) I I

50. In a PPI display, the sweep, noise and range markers appear, but no targets are present. One possible cause might be a:
(a) defective receiver klystron.
(b) defective magnetron.
(c) defective synchronizer.
(d) defective duplexer.
(e) Both (a) and (b) are true.

(a) I I   (b) I I   (c) I I   (d) I I   (e) I I

Element 8, Test 2

1. If the reflecting surface of a radar set's parabolic dish is coated with a thin layer of dirt:
(a) there will be little or no effect on the set's performance.
(b) the beam width will be much increased.
(c) the target echoes will be weaker.
(d) the pulse shape will be distorted.
(e) there will be a severe mismatch between the guide and the reflector.

(a) I I   (b) I I   (c) I I   (d) I I   (e) I I

2. When using a PPI display, the echo from the receiver may be applied to the CRT's:
(a) y plates.   (b) x plates.   (c) grid.
(d) vertical deflecting coils.
(e) horizontal deflecting coils.

(a) I I   (b) I I   (c) I I   (d) I I   (e) I I

3. A choke joint:
(a) is used when two waveguide sections are fed in parallel.
(b) must never be used with rotating waveguide sections.
(c) has two flanges which may be mechanically separated by several centimeters.
(d) presents an inductive impedance to the waveguide.
(e) None of the above are true.

(a) I I   (b) I I   (c) I I   (d) I I   (e) I I

4. In which of the following stages of a pulse radar set may a rotary spark gap be found?
(a) The local oscillator.
(b) The modulator unit.
(c) The transmitter's oscillator stage.
(d) The duplexer.
(e) The calibrator unit.

(a) I I   (b) I I   (c) I I   (d) I I   (e) I I

5. The circuit shown in Fig. 1 represents:
(a) a video amplifier with negative feedback.
(b) a multivibrator.
(c) a sawtooth generator.
(d) a synchronized blocking oscillator.
(e) an Armstrong pulse generator.

(a) I I   (b) I I   (c) I I   (d) I I   (e) I I

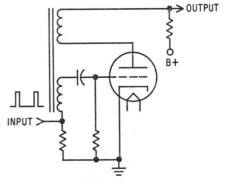

FIGURE 1

6. Which entry is not required in the installation and maintenance records of a ship radar station?
(a) The range of the radar installed.
(b) The date and place of initial installation.
(c) Any necessary steps taken to remedy any interference found to exist at the time of such installation.
(d) The reason for the trouble leading to a complaint, including the name of any component or component part which failed or was maladjusted.
(e) The name, license number, and date of the ship radar operator endorsement on the first or second class radio operator license of the responsible operator performing or immediately supervising the installation, servicing, or maintenance.

(a) I I   (b) I I   (c) I I   (d) I I   (e) I I

7. For a radar set operating near 9 GHz, a typical frequency for the receiver's IF would be:
(a) 455 kHz   (b) 1 MHz   (c) 60 MHz
(d) 5 MHz   (e) 10.7 MHz

(a) I I   (b) I I   (c) I I   (d) I I   (e) I I

8. The parabolic dish of a radar set's antenna system is used to:

113

(a) provide an impedance match between the waveguide and free space.
(b) eliminate the necessity for separate transmitter and receiver antenna systems.
(c) reduce the antenna gain and therefore broaden the frequency response of the antenna system.
(d) provide a wide beam for good surface coverage.
(e) concentrate the RF energy from the waveguide into a unidirectional narrow beam.

(a) I I   (b) I I   (c) I I   (d) I I   (e) I I

9. If the range of a target is 7.5 nautical miles, what is the time interval between the radar pulse being transmitted and the target echo being received?
(a) 46.5 μ sec   (b) 93.0 μ sec
(c) 18.5 μ sec   (d) 70.0 μ sec
(e) 23.0 μ sec

(a) I I   (b) I I   (c) I I   (d) I I   (e) I I

10. In a pulse marine radar set used for navigation, the measurement of the range of a target is normally associated with a time interval that is on the order of:
(a) picoseconds.   (b) nanoseconds.
(c) microseconds.   (d) milliseconds.
(e) 10^{-7} second.

(a) I I   (b) I I   (c) I I   (d) I I   (e) I I

11. Which of the following stages of a radar set may be represented by the circuit shown in Fig. 2?
(a) A compensated video amplifier.
(b) An IF amplifier.   (c) A modulator unit.
(d) A pulse shaping circuit.
(e) An AFC discriminator.

(a) I I   (b) I I   (c) I I   (d) I I   (e) I I

12. A shipboard radar set is operating on 5550 MHz. What is the wavelength of its transmission?
(a) 5.4 cm   (b) 1.85 cm   (c) 0.0167 cm
(d) 18.5 cm   (e) 9.25 cm

(a) I I   (b) I I   (c) I I   (d) I I   (e) I I

13. A weak magnetron magnet may cause:
(a) arcing in the modulator tube.
(b) excessive RF output from the magnetron.
(c) the magnetron undercurrent relay to drop out.
(d) the magnetron current meter to show an increase.
(e) None of the above are true.

(a) I I   (b) I I   (c) I I   (d) I I   (e) I I

14. The effect of "sea return":
(a) limits the maximum range available.
(b) limits the target discrimination for distant echoes.
(c) may be reduced by the STC system.

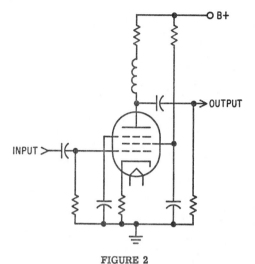

FIGURE 2

(d) limits the detection of targets at close ranges.
(e) Both (c) and (d) are true.

(a) I I   (b) I I   (c) I I   (d) I I   (e) I I

15. The bearing resolution of a radar set is mainly determined by the:
(a) transmitted antenna beam width.
(b) pulse duration.
(c) magnetron frequency.
(d) antenna rotation rate.
(e) All the above are true.

(a) I I   (b) I I   (c) I I   (d) I I   (e) I I

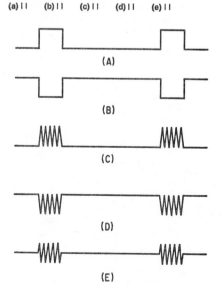

FIGURE 3

16. Which of the waveforms shown in Fig. 3 best represents the output from the magnetron to the waveguide?

(a) I I   (b) I I   (c) I I   (d) I I   (e) I I

17. A rectangular waveguide may have its inside walls silver-plated in order to:
(a) increase the VSWR.
(b) improve conducting properties.
(c) assure a smooth interior surface.
(d) prevent twisting of the wave's polarization.
(e) Both (b) and (c) are true.

(a) I I   (b) I I   (c) I I   (d) I I   (e) I I

18. How would an operator of a loran set determine if interference is being caused by a radar set?
(a) Vertical pulses or "spikes" moving across the scope screen.
(b) Hash or "grass" in the vicinity of the scanning lines.
(c) Round or circular patterns appearing on the screen.
(d) Horizontal lines appearing on the screen.
(e) Both (a) and (b) are true.

(a) I I   (b) I I   (c) I I   (d) I I   (e) I I

19. The communications technician, while checking radio communications equipment aboard ship, should remember that:
(a) radar RF pulses are essentially sinusoidal in shape and therefore will not cause interference.
(b) pulse modulated RF waves will not cause interference.
(c) pulse modulated RF waves are rich in modulation frequency harmonics and will generally cause radio interference.
(d) the highly directive antenna of a radar system makes interference in radio communications receivers a very remote possibility.
(e) radar RF pulses are of such short dura-

tion they cannot interfere with lower frequency communications receivers.

(a) I I   (b) I I   (c) I I   (d) I I   (e) I I

20. If the pulse width of a radar set is increased (keeping all other parameters the same) the:
(a) target resolution will improve.
(b) minimum range at which targets may be detected will increase.
(c) average power will be reduced.
(d) bandwidth of the echo (received signal) will be decreased.
(e) maximum target range available will be reduced.

(a) I I   (b) I I   (c) I I   (d) I I   (e) I I

21. In a radar receiver, the reflex klystron may be coarse tuned by:
(a) adjusting a trimmer capacitor placed across the mouth of the cavity.
(b) controlling the voltage of the cavity grids.
(c) mechanically altering the position of the repeller.
(d) adjusting the flexible wall of the cavity.
(e) Both (b) and (d) are true.

(a) I I   (b) I I   (c) I I   (d) I I   (e) I I

22. The block diagram shown in Fig. 4 is of a SHF marine pulse radar receiver. The block marked "A" represents the:
(a) signal discriminator.
(b) local oscillator.
(c) signal crystal mixer.
(d) microwave preamplifier.
(e) AFC crystal detector stage.

(a) I I   (b) I I   (c) I I   (d) I I   (e) I I

23. In the block diagram of Fig. 4, block "B" represents the:
(a) signal crystal mixer.
(b) second detector stage.
(c) signal discriminator.
(d) local oscillator.

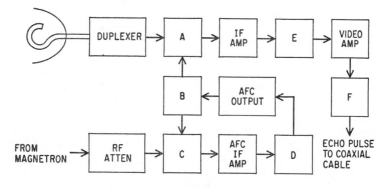

FIGURE 4

(e) AFC crystal detector stage.

(a) I I   (b) I I   (c) I I   (d) I I   (e) I I

24. In the block diagram of Fig. 4, block "C"
represents the:
(a) signal crystal mixer.
(b) local oscillator.
(c) AFC discriminator.
(d) second detector stage.
(e) AFC crystal detector stage.

(a) I I   (b) I I   (c) I I   (d) I I   (e) I I

25. In the block diagram of Fig. 4, block "D"
represents the:
(a) local oscillator.
(b) AFC discriminator.
(c) AFC limiter stage.
(d) AFC final IF amplifier.
(e) reflex klystron stage.

(a) I I   (b) I I   (c) I I   (d) I I   (e) I I

26. In the block diagram of Fig. 4, block "E"
represents the:
(a) signal discriminator stage.
(b) crystal mixer stage.
(c) receiver second detector stage.
(d) signal limiter stage.
(e) AFC crystal detector stage.

(a) I I   (b) I I   (c) I I   (d) I I   (e) I I

27. In the block diagram of Fig. 4, block "F"
represents the:
(a) high gain video amplifier stage.
(b) compensated video power amplifier stage.
(c) pulse shaping amplifier stage.
(d) noise limiter stage.
(e) emitter or cathode follower stage.

(a) I I   (b) I I   (c) I I   (d) I I   (e) I I

28. The pulse repetition time is:
(a) the reciprocal of the pulse frequency.
(b) the reciprocal of the pulse width.
(c) equal to the pulse width divided by the
     pulse frequency.
(d) equal to the pulse width times the duty
     cycle.
(e) equal to the duty cycle divided by the
     pulse width.

(a) I I   (b) I I   (c) I I   (d) I I   (e) I I

29. If the pulse width of a radar set is 1
μ sec and the pulse repetition rate is 500 per
second, what is the bandwidth required by the
radar receiver?
(a) 1 kHz   (b) 500 kHz   (c) 2 MHz
(d) 5 MHz   (e) 10 MHz

(a) I I   (b) I I   (c) I I   (d) I I   (e) I I

30. The magnetron in a radar set functions
as a:
(a) modulator tube.
(b) transmitter oscillator.
(c) pulse generator.
(d) magnetic amplifier.
(e) local oscillator.

(a) I I   (b) I I   (c) I I   (d) I I   (e) I I

31. In a radar transmitter the pulse width
is 1.0 μ sec. The pulse frequency is 500 Hz,
and the peak power output is 200 kW. What
is the value of the average power?
(a) 10 W   (b) 20 W   (c) 50 W
(d) 100 W   (e) 200 W

(a) I I   (b) I I   (c) I I   (d) I I   (e) I I

32. Which of the following items of equipment
might be affected by radar interference?
(a) Communications receivers.
(b) Loran.   (c) Auto-alarm systems.
(d) Direction finders.
(e) All of the above are true.

(a) I I   (b) I I   (c) I I   (d) I I   (e) I I

33. What is the pulse repetition time of a
radar set that has a pulse repetition rate of
500 Hz?
(a) 50,000 μ sec   (b) 1000 μ sec
(c) 2 milliseconds   (d) 500 μ sec
(e) 5 milliseconds

(a) I I   (b) I I   (c) I I   (d) I I   (e) I I

34. The block diagram in Fig. 5 represents
the AFC system of a radar receiver. Which
stage does block "A" represent?
(a) AFC crystal detector.   (b) TR switch.
(c) AFC RF amplifier.
(d) ratio detector.   (e) AFC limiter.

(a) I I   (b) I I   (c) I I   (d) I I   (e) I I

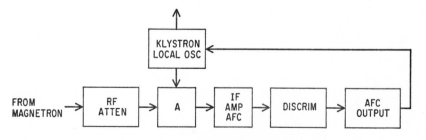

FIGURE 5

35. During the normal course of service, who may operate radar equipment in the Ship Service?
(a) Only the licensed radio operator on duty.
(b) The master of the ship or any person designated by him.
(c) Only the helmsman.
(d) Only a ship's officer.
(e) None of the above are true.

(a) I I   (b) I I   (c) I I   (d) I I   (e) I I

36. In a pulse radar system, the repetition rate means the:
(a) antenna rotation rate.
(b) rate at which the klystron is frequency modulated by the AFC system.
(c) reciprocal of the pulse duration.
(d) number of pulses transmitted in one second.
(e) reciprocal of the duty cycle.

(a) I I   (b) I I   (c) I I   (d) I I   (e) I I

37. How may interference from a radar set be recognized by a person listening to a communications receiver?
(a) There will be a continuous whistle of varying pitch in the receiver's output.
(b) There will be a steady tone present in the receiver's output.
(c) There will be noise or hash in the receiver's output.
(d) The receiver's selectivity will be reduced.
(e) Both (b) and (c) are true.

(a) I I   (b) I I   (c) I I   (d) I I   (e) I I

38. The intensity of the echoes on the PPI display depends on the:
(a) pulse repetition rate.
(b) pulse shape.
(c) transmitted radio frequency.
(d) antenna rotation speed.
(e) Both (a) and (d) are true.

(a) I I   (b) I I   (c) I I   (d) I I   (e) I I

39. In a radar set, the magnetron frequency has drifted from 3005 to 3004 MHz, and the output frequency of the reflex klystron is 2975 MHz. If the receiver's IF is 30 MHz, the output from the AFC discriminator will:
(a) shift the klystron's frequency to 2974 MHz.
(b) cause the electrons to spend a shorter time in the space between the cavity and the repeller-plate.
(c) shift the klystron's frequency to 2976 MHz.
(d) make the repeller's potential more positive with respect to ground.
(e) Both (a) and (b) are true.

(a) I I   (b) I I   (c) I I   (d) I I   (e) I I

40. The purpose of the polystyrene window placed across the end of the waveguide is:

(a) to increase the power output.
(b) to match the waveguide impedance to the impedance of free space.
(c) to form the radiated electromagnetic energy into a narrow beam.
(d) to increase the value of the VSWR in the waveguide.
(e) Both (a) and (b) are true.

(a) I I   (b) I I   (c) I I   (d) I I   (e) I I

41. Precautions to be taken with a magnetron include which of the following?
(a) Never operate the magnetron without the magnet in position.
(b) Never subject the magnet to extreme heat.
(c) Never subject the magnet to mechanical shock.
(d) Keep all magnetic materials such as tools away from the immediate vicinity of the magnet.
(e) All the above are true.

(a) I I   (b) I I   (c) I I   (d) I I   (e) I I

42. Under what circumstances may a person who does not hold a radio operator's license operate a radar station in the Ship Service?
(a) When the frequency-determining device of the magnetron oscillator is a non-tunable pulse type, the radar requires only the use of external controls, and the Master has given authorization.
(b) Only when the equipment has been serviced by a licensed operator, and the licensed operator is off duty.
(c) When the licensed operator is off duty, and the unlicensed person is a U.S. citizen.
(d) When it is not convenient to obtain the Master's permission to operate the equipment.
(e) None of the above are true.

(a) I I   (b) I I   (c) I I   (d) I I   (e) I I

43. In a ship radar system, who is authorized to replace receiver tubes and fuses?
(a) only someone who holds a radar endorsement.
(b) Only a First Class Radio Telephone Licensee.
(c) Only a Second Class Radio Telephone Licensee.
(d) Only a Second Class Radio Telegraph Licensee.
(e) Anyone can replace receiver tubes and fuses.

(a) I I   (b) I I   (c) I I   (d) I I   (e) I I

44. Which of the following frequency bands has been allocated to ship radar transmitters?
(a) 1900 to 2100 MHz
(b) 5460 to 5650 MHz
(c) 3900 to 4100 MHz
(d) 8300 to 8500 MHz

(e) 10,300 to 10,500 MHz

(a) I I   (b) I I   (c) I I   (d) I I   (e) I I

45. In a pulse radar set, a discriminator is used in the:
(a) AFC system.   (b) STC system.
(c) second detector stage of the radar receiver.
(d) duplexer unit.
(e) mixer stage of the radar receiver.

(a) I I   (b) I I   (c) I I   (d) I I   (e) I I

46. The duty cycle is equal to:
(a) peak power/average power.
(b) pulse repetition time/pulse width.
(c) pulse repetition time multiplied by pulse width.
(d) pulse width multiplied by pulse frequency.
(e) the reciprocal of c.

(a) I I   (b) I I   (c) I I   (d) I I   (e) I I

47. Bright flashing pie sections which appear on a radar's PPI display may most likely be caused by a:
(a) defective signal mixer diode.
(b) defective duplexer.
(c) defective magnetron.
(d) weak magnetron magnet.
(e) defective crystal in the AFC circuit.

(a) I I   (b) I I   (c) I I   (d) I I   (e) I I

48. Klystrons are generally used in the frequency range of:
(a) 500 MHz to 3 GHz
(b) 3 to 30 GHz
(c) 600 MHz to 30 GHz
(d) 60 MHz to 60 GHz
(e) 300 MHz to 6 GHz

(a) I I   (b) I I   (c) I I   (d) I I   (e) I I

49. Pulse radar may be used to determine the:
(a) range of a target.
(b) direction in which the target is moving.
(c) bearing of a target.
(d) speed of a target.
(e) All the above are true.

(a) I I   (b) I I   (c) I I   (d) I I   (e) I I

50. The aquadag coating on the inside of a PPI display tube is used:
(a) to focus the beam of primary electrons.
(b) as a second anode.
(c) to provide a return path for secondary electrons emitted from the screen.
(d) to shield the electron beam from all magnetic fields.
(e) Both (b) and (c) are true.

(a) I I   (b) I I   (c) I I   (d) I I   (e) I I